STEWART

99BB
1400

# ARTIFICIAL

# INTELLIGENCE TECHNIQUES

E. B. Carne

Spartan Division (Books, Inc.)
*Washington, D. C.*

Macmillan and Company, Ltd.
*London*

*To Joan*

Library of Congress Catalog Card No. 65-27043

Sole distributors in Great Britain, the British
Commonwealth and the Continent of Europe:

Macmillan and Company, Ltd.
4 Little Essex Street
London, W. C. 2

# PREFACE

The motivation for this book is a desire to provide a practical summary of electronic techniques for simulating human intelligence which will be of use to a general engineering audience familiar with the rudiments of logic and computers. It is a book for the electronic engineer or scientist who is anxious to delve into a new field which may one day change our modern technology in much the same way as the first electronic computers, ENIAC, EDVAC, SEAC, and their successors, revolutionized the technical world of the late 1940's and 1950's. In selecting material, I have steered clear of many theoretical topics which are of interest only to a few mathematicians and of studies which appear to have been prepared by those who look upon artificial intelligence as an excuse for introducing new terms, new symbols and new algebras.

It is particularly unfortunate that many well-informed and capable persons hold the opinion that our subject contains *too much blackboard and not enough breadboard.* In fact, there is a wealth of practical information scattered in various technical journals, symposium proceedings and reports, waiting for those who have the opportunity to apply it. Wherever possible, reference has been made to these publications so that the interested reader can pursue particular topics in greater detail. It is hoped that the presentation is neither too elementary nor too difficult. Certainly a great deal more could have been included in the way of mathematical proofs of sufficiency, convergence, etc. However this would detract from the major objective of presenting the concepts in a relatively unsophisticated manner for the general technical reader.

Some of the work reported in Chapters 2 and 3 was done by the author and his colleagues in the Advanced Computer Laboratory, Computer Department, Melpar, Inc., with the support of the Bionics and Computer Branch, Electronic Technology Laboratory, Air Force Systems Command, under Contracts AF33(616)-7834 and AF33(616)-7682. Thanks are due to Air Force Systems Command for permission to publish the results. Review of this material does not imply Department of Defense endorsement of factual accuracy or opinion. The programs were directed by Mr. Cecil W. Gwinn. It is a pleasure to acknowledge his advice, assistance, and constant enthusiasm in pursuit of a better understanding of bionics.

Some of the other work (reported in parts of Chapters 3 and 4) was done under research programs supported by company funds. Thanks are due to Melpar, Inc., for permission to use this data and for support during the preparation of the manuscript.

The publications of many people have contributed to the subject matter. Specific acknowledgment is due:

Control Data Corporation for permission to use data from *Programming Manual 145c Rev. 10/62, OSAS-A/160-A Assembly System 507a 11/62,* and *160 FORTRAN/Reference Manual 4/62* for their 160A Computer.

Institute of Electrical and Electronic Engineers for permission to use data from:
  1. "The Simulation of Neural Elements by Electrical Networks Based on Multi-Aperture Magnetic Cores" A.E. Brain, *Proceedings, IRE* vol. 49, 1961, pp. 49–52.
  2. "Neuristor—A Novel Device and System Concept," H. D. Crane, *Proceedings, IRE* vol. 50, 1962, pp. 2048–2060.
  3. "An Active Pulse Transmission Line Simulating Nerve Axon," J. Nagumo, S. Arimoto, S. Yoshizawa, *Proceedings, IRE* vol. 50, 1962, pp. 2061–2070.

McGraw-Hill Book Co. for permission to use data from:
  "Image Processing and Functional Retina Synthesis," E. E. Loebner, *Human Factors in Technology*, E. Bennett, J. Degan, J. Spiegel, eds, 1963, pp 492–518.

Pergamon Press, Inc., for permission to use data from:
  "Properties of a Neuron with Many Inputs," M. Blum
and
  "The Neuristor," H. D. Crane, in *Principles of Self-Organization,* H. von Foerster, G. W. Zopf, eds., 1962, proceedings of a symposium sponsored by the University of Illinois.

Plenum Press, Inc., for permission to use data from:
  1. "Storage and Manipulation of Information in Random Networks," R. A. Beurle, *Aspects of the Theory of Artificial Intelligence*, C. A. Muses, ed, 1962, pp 19–42.
  2. "A Self-Organizing Binary Logical Element," E. B. Carne, E. M. Connelly, P. H. Halpern, B. A. Logan, *Biological Prototypes and Synthetic Systems,* vol 1, E. E. Bernard, M. R. Kare, eds, 1962, pp 311–330.

Spartan Books, for permission to use data from:
  1. *Principles of Neurodynamics*, F. Rosenblatt, 1962.
  2. "Tolerable Errors of Neurons for Infallible Nets," M. Blum,

N. M. Onesto, L. A. M. Verbeek, *Redundancy Techniques for Computing Systems*, R. H. Wilcox, W. C. Mann, eds, 1962, pp 66–69.

By their readiness to enter into discussion, many former associates at Melpar, Inc., have unknowingly participated in the preparation of this book. In this respect, I am particularly indebted to Mr. P. H. Halpern, Mr. W. H. Fuhr, Mr. E. M. Connelly, Dr. K. E. Justice, and Dr. J. G. Cole. Thanks are also due to Mr. R. R. Townsend, Jr., for assistance with the programs in Chapter 5, and to Mr. S. Y. Lim for assistance in the preparation of the many illustrations. Finally, I should like to give special thanks to Mrs. M. R. Peebles for patiently typing and retyping the manuscript and for being her charming self throughout its preparation.

E. B. CARNE
*Greenville, Texas*

# TABLE OF CONTENTS

Chapter 1

# INTRODUCTION

Not so long ago, the possibility of endowing machines with a capacity to learn and to operate in an intelligent manner was restricted to science fiction. With the advent of modern electronics, however, it is not only possible but perhaps necessary to construct devices which can substitute for a human operator in routine circumstances and to consider the larger problem of building devices which can simulate the more complex aspects of human intelligence.

As an example, one of the major developments of the twentieth century is the electronic computer. More specifically it is the digital computer, whose speed and general purpose versatility have been responsible for much of our current technology. Using components which operate at microsecond speeds to perform addition, subtraction, and storage of information, computers perform tasks previously considered uneconomical because of the sheer magnitude of the human effort required or because the result was out of date before it could be produced.

Digital computers operate on the basis of binary signals arranged in proper sequence. Before the data can be manipulated it must be reduced to correctly coded messages. This can be done by a human operator who produces the code on a punched card, for instance, or by some form of sensor system which provides coded samples of the environment. In applications such as accounting and inventory control, and in many scientific areas, the raw data is already in numerical form and can be entered easily into the computer. In others, however, the data may be a portion of a photograph or map, or it may be written or printed material from which certain items must be extracted. Human knowledge and intelligence are required to perform recognition, selection, and perhaps correlation before this data is ready for computer insertion. This takes a great deal of a skilled analyst's time and is a very definite deterrent to undertaking many worthwhile tasks.

The full utilization of a digital computer is further complicated because the programming, i.e., instructing the machine in the details of its work, becomes more complex as the applications become more ambitious. In fact, in many cases the human programmer is hard pressed to reduce the

1

broad concepts of operation into detailed flow diagrams and thence into a flawless sequence of instructions to accommodate the many different sets of conditions which may be included.

It would be a considerable improvement in the electronic computer art if a machine could be endowed with the capability to operate on pictorial inputs, recognizing, selecting, and correlating that data which is pertinent to the current problem, *and* to generate its own program in response to general instruction. Both of these functions are presently performed by a human analyst, drawing on past teaching and experience. Oftentimes he uses *trial and error,* sometimes *intuition,* and at other times *logical deduction.* At all times the operation is time-consuming and prone to error even when performed by the most conscientious person, since we all have many other interests which tend to distract us. One of the great virtues of a machine is that it is not interested in the state of the weather, the World Series, or the size of its paycheck. Since modern computer problems may well run to hundreds of thousands of instructions and require the assimilation of data at a rate of a million or more bits per second, such single-mindedness has an economic advantage.

There are many other fields in which the intelligent operation of machines would improve and enlarge our technological capacity. Thus we can speculate on the utility of a device capable of reading an article in Russian or Chinese, for example, and printing out a flawless translation in English—or better still, an English summary; or it might be an unmanned space probe which can reconnoiter, observe, and investigate phenomena as they occur in deep space, returning later with a report such as one would expect from a human observer.

In many of our successful imitations of nature it is not the detailed mechanism but the end function which we seek to reproduce; thus, airplanes have only a passing similarity to birds, light is made without the combustion of organic materials, electric current is generated without lightning strokes, and complex polymers are made without photosynthesis. Likewise, it should be possible to imitate the rudiments of learning without building a human brain.

In *Summa Theologica,* the thirteenth century Dominican scholar, St. Thomas Aquinas, attributes three major components to the human intellect: passive (intellectus possibilis); active (intellectus agens); and will. The *passive intellect* renders sensory inputs intelligible, contains the memory, and is the repository of our learning (experience). It provides the ability to recall actions and their consequences so that, when we are confronted with a specific set of circumstances, this information can be used to formulate a strategy for the present case. The *active intellect* develops abstract concepts such as beauty, loyalty, God, and the like. The *will* provides motivation for intellectual activity. The greater portion of man's intelligent acts are concerned with the *passive intellect*, and it is this function which can be simulated most easily by a machine.

The study of intelligent machines may be considered to fall within the interdisciplinary field of *bionics* (from Greek *bion* = living and *-ic* = like, or study of), which has been defined as "The science and technology devoted to the study and analysis of living systems and the physical realization of the more sophisticated functions of these...systems."[22] Some workers use the term *electrology* (electronic biology). The results of work performed in many basic disciplines are included. Anatomists, physiologists and biologists have contributed knowledge pertaining to the physical structure of man and animals, and a description of the living nervous system; psychologists have added data concerning learning mechanisms, motivation, and goals; and mathematicians, physicists, and engineers have attempted to formalize these ideas and to reduce them to electronic models. The aim is to devise machines which can adequately perform those functions which are the products of early teaching, learning, and experience. Such is not within our grasp at the present; however, a beginning has been made—albeit a very rudimentary first step, considering our objective—and it is the purpose of this book to present some of the results.

## INTELLIGENCE AND LEARNING

Intelligence and learning are interwoven, the one being the prerequisite, as it were, of the other. Perhaps the basic attribute of an intelligent organism is its capability to learn to perform various functions within a changing environment so as to survive and to prosper. Many feats of skill and understanding are learned before a child grows into a man ready to compete for a place in the world. Unfortunately, once learned, some of these feats become commonplace, almost unnoticed, and so are not regarded as particularly remarkable when imitated by a machine.

As we shall see, experience-type behavior can be learned by machines. Such devices are capable of performing useful functions in a much shorter time and far more reliably than a human operator. However, there is a great gap between these machines and machines which might be capable of forming concepts, making inductive inferences, and the like. A moment's reflection will show that portions of the definition* on the next page (particularly **1b**) are consistent with a mechanical simulation.

---

*By permission. From *Webster's Third New International Dictionary,* copyright 1961 by G & C Merriam Co., Publishers of the Merriam-Webster Dictionaries.

¹in·tel·li·gence \ən·'teləjən(t)s\ *n* -s *often attrib* [ME, fr. MF, fr. OF, fr. L *intelligentia*, fr. *intelligent-, intelligens* (pres. part.) + *-ia -y* — more at INTELLIGENT] **1 a** (1) **:** the faculty of understanding **:** capacity to know or apprehend **:** INTELLECT, REASON ⟨∼, which emerged during the revolutionary cycles of matter as the highest form yet achieved —Hermann Reith⟩ ⟨conceived of history as the expression of a divine ∼⟩ (2) *Christian Science* **:** the basic eternal quality of divine Mind **b :** the available ability as measured by intelligence tests or by other social criteria to use one's existing knowledge to meet new situations and to solve new problems, to learn, to foresee problems, to use symbols or relationships, to create new re-lationships, to think abstractly **:** ability to perceive one's en-vironment, to deal with it symbolically, to deal with it effec-tively, to adjust to it, to work toward a goal **:** the degree of one's alertness, awareness, or acuity **:** ability to use with awareness the mechanism of reasoning whether conceived as a unified intellectual factor or as the aggregate of many intellec-tual factors or abilities, as intuitive or as analytic, as organ-ismic, biological, physiological, psychological, or social in origin and nature **c :** mental acuteness **:** SAGACITY, SHREWD-NESS ⟨did all he was asked to do with ∼ and great good humor⟩ **2 a :** an intelligent being; *esp* **:** an incorporeal spirit **:** ANGEL ⟨hierarchies of angelic ∼*s* —S.F.Mason⟩ **b :** a per-son of some intellectual capacity ⟨all those ∼*s* we have agreed to call great —*Times Lit. Supp.*⟩ ⟨the greatest all-round ∼ writing in England —P.S.O'Hegarty⟩ **3 a :** the act of under-standing **:** COMPREHENSION, KNOWLEDGE ⟨faith is necessary to the ∼ of the Christian mysteries —*Encyc. Americana*⟩ **b** (1) **:** information communicated **:** NEWS, NOTICE, ADVICE ⟨more weight is laid upon ∼ than on editorials —Horace Greeley⟩ ⟨the joyful ∼ that there is hope —Georgina Grahame⟩ ⟨from the engine-room voice tube came ∼ of more importance — M.S.Boylan⟩ (2) **:** interchange of information **:** COMMUNICA-TION ⟨accused of maintaining ∼ with the enemy⟩ (3) *obs* **:** a piece of information — usu. used in pl. (4) *archaic* **:** common understanding or mutual relations **:** ACQUAINTANCE, INTER-COURSE (5) **:** evaluated information concerning an enemy or possible enemy or a possible theater of operations and the conclusions drawn therefrom; *also* **:** the section, agency, or persons engaged in obtaining such information **:** SECRET SERVICE ⟨investigated me and told me I was qualified for Navy ∼ —T.F.Murphy⟩ ⟨an ∼ bureau⟩ ⟨available to American and allied ∼ organizations —L.W.Doob⟩ **syn** see MIND

There is no doubt that a number of machines can be built, using some-what different principles, which can identify the terms of Maxwell's equa-tions as they are printed in a standard textbook. Certain of these ma-chines might also be able to identify the terms unequivocally when presented with a different textbook, and perhaps one of the machines might be able to identify the terms of a carefully handwritten set of these equations. However, none would be able to recognize the essential equivalence of the integral and derivative forms (i.e., two ways of de-scribing the same thing) nor, given the work of Ampère and Faraday, could they perform the formalization effected by Maxwell in establishing these expressions.

Some of the basic acts which one might expect an intelligent machine to perform are *recognizing, deciding,* and *predicting.* They may be defined as follows.

**Recognizing:** The occurrence of a given phenomenon will produce a set of signals $i_i$ as outputs of a particular sensor system. The number of sig-nals, their individual configuration, and their information content (some may be redundant) will be a direct function of the sensor system used. At some time in the past, standard phenomena $A, B, \ldots$ etc., will have been used to develop sets of descriptors $a_i, b_i, \ldots$ etc. for the same sensor system. The process of recognition is the process of mapping, $i_i$ onto $a_i$, $b_i,$ ... etc., to determine which is *closest*. Thus, if

$$S(a_i, i_i), \quad S(b_i, i_i), \ldots > S(p_i, i_i), \tag{1.1}$$

where $S$ represents the operation of determining the distance between the signal sets, the phenomenon giving rise to the signals $i_i$ will be uniquely recognized as the standard phenomenon $P$.

The distance between two digital signals, $F_1(x_1 x_2 \ldots x_n)$ and $F_2(x_1 x_2 \ldots x_n)$, is

$$S(F_1, F_2) = N(F_1 * F_2), \tag{1.2}$$

where $N(F_1 * F_2)$ is the number of minterms in the *exclusive-or* $F_1 * F_2$. This definition obeys the usual metric properties, i.e.,

$$\begin{aligned}
&1. \ S(F_1, F_2) = S(F_2, F_1) \\
&2. \ S(F_1, F_2) > 0 \quad \text{when} \quad F_1 \neq F_2 \\
&\phantom{2. \ S(F_1, F_2)} = 0 \quad \text{when} \quad F_1 = F_2 \\
&3. \ S(F_1, F_2) + S(F_1, F_3) \geq S(F_2, F_3)
\end{aligned} \tag{1.3}$$

If a complete signal set is not available (due to malfunction of parts of the sensor system, perhaps), the standard phenomenon selected will be that which is closest on the basis of those components of the set which are present. This may lead to the selection of a group of standard phenomena, $P, Q, R, \ldots$ etc., each of which gives rise to a similar truncated signal set. A substantial change in the sensor system will require re-presentation of the standard phenomenon to establish new standard descriptor sets.

**Deciding:** A decision is the selection of a particular action when several alternatives are presented. If the current situation is characterized by a signal set $x_i$ and the alternative actions are described by signal sets $_1 y_i, \, _2 y_i, \ldots$ etc., a number of decisions is possible:

$$_1 y_i = D_1(x_i); \quad _2 y_i = D_2(x_i); \quad \text{etc.}, \tag{1.4}$$

where $D$ represents the decision transform. In general, the selection of the alternative action is made on the basis of the current situation, an ultimate objective or goal, and experience of similar situations in the past. Under these conditions, the appropriate decision $D_0$ (optimum decision) is that which selects the alternative action $(_0 y_i)$ which is closest to that action which would immediately implement the goal $(g_i)$, i.e.,

$$_0 y_i = D_0(x_i) \tag{1.5}$$

$$S(_1 y_i, g_i), \quad S(_2 y_i, g_i) \ldots > S(_0 y_i, g_i) \tag{1.6}$$

In any particular case, the signal set $g_i$ might be one of the alternatives available on the occurrence of $x_i$.

**Predicting:** In its simplest terms, prediction is the anticipation of an event, given the preceding event. Thus, if certain events occur which give rise to sets of signals $_{n-1}i_i, {_n}i_i, {_{n+1}}i_i, \ldots$ etc., prediction is the selection of a transform $P$ such that

$$
\begin{aligned}
{_n}i_i &= {_{(n-1)}}P_n({_{(n-1)}}i_i), \\
{_{(n+1)}}i_i &= {_n}P_{(n+1)}({_n}i_i), \text{ etc.}
\end{aligned}
\tag{1.7}
$$

For regular series $_{(n-1)}P_n = {_n}P_{(n+1)}$, etc. For irregular series, the transforms might be expected to be different. Prediction, as defined above, can be regarded as a special case of decision making in which the optimum decision is that which predicts the next event correctly. More sophisticated prediction involves the use of a number of preceding terms, i.e.,

$$
{_n}i_i = F[{_{(n-1)}}P_n({_{(n-1)}}i_i), {_{(n-2)}}P_{(n-1)}({_{(n-2)}}i_i), \ldots \text{ etc.}]
\tag{1.8}
$$

Once again, for a regular series, the successive transforms could be expected to be regular, so that

$$
{_n}i_i = F[P_1({_{(n-1)}}i_i), P_2({_{(n-2)}}i_i), \ldots \text{ etc.}],
\tag{1.9}
$$

where $P_n$ is the transformation between the predicted term and the $n^{\text{th}}$ antecedent.

Intelligent machines are often referred to as *self-organizing systems*. In the strict sense of the words, such machines cannot exist since they would have to operate without external motivation of any kind.[2] However, if external motivation is allowed, so that the system can be provided with criteria with which to evaluate its response, learning can occur.

At first, the system's view of the external world will be meaningless; then, after a period of random changes, suitable connectives may begin to form which provide an appropriate response to the various stimuli. By exploratory interaction with the environment, features of the input information gradually take on significance, and various forms of association may occur which assist in the selection of the proper rejoinder. At a somewhat later stage, the system may develop the ability to concentrate on important features while ignoring the remainder and to recognize the same features in several signals; such behavior is usually called *generalization*. At a still later stage of learning, a similar metamorphosis *may* lead to *abstraction;* however, no experimental example of this type of behavior has, as yet, been demonstrated.

An important point which is often ignored, particularly by those who wish to see a closer analogy between human capability and present-day machines, is that the human learning process makes use of continuity.[1] No one event stands alone. It depends on the immediate past and past history, and is part of the total environment, whereas many of the systems to be discussed depend solely on the recognition of discrete situations.

Modern psychology provides a number of competing theories to explain how the human mind learns the myriad facts and responses necessary for day-to-day living. The least sophisticated theory (and perhaps the least acceptable to the psychologist) is a simple stimulus-response mechanism. In this, the organism develops a discrete response to each unique stimulus. The response is compared to the response which is desired by an external *teacher* or by an internal goal, and the organism is *rewarded* or *punished* depending on the degree of validity of the response. The organism eventually *adapts* so as to produce the desired output more often than not.

Hull, in a more ambitious theory,[17] uses the concepts of *habit strength* and *drive reduction.* Habit strength is a measure of the organization established in the nervous system by reinforcement. Up to a limit it is a function of the number of reinforcements; beyond this, no further increase is possible. Drive reduction is the reduction of a neural state accompanying a need; greater drive reduction implies progress towards the satisfaction of a need. In this theory, learning is an inverse function of the time lapse between a stimulus and the desired response; it also depends on the time lapse between the response and the reinforcement. Habits are formed and increase in strength in proportion to the number of reinforcements and the amount of need reduction produced. Habit strength is a function of the number of rewarded trials; it may increase or remain the same, but is never reduced. Unrewarded trials increase *reactive* and *conditioned inhibition.* Reactive inhibition represents a decay such as will occur due to fatigue of the organism. Conditioned inhibition is produced by a positive teaching for the organism to respond oppositely to the response originally taught.

A response which has been *completely learned* is characterized by maximum habit strength; it can be completely extinguished by producing maximum conditioned inhibition. The learning process depends on the concept that organisms have innate general responses which are controlled by needs, and that such responses have relatively high probabilities of terminating the specific need. When a stimulus and a response occur in close contiguity and need is reduced, an increment is added to the habit strength of the appropriate stimulus-response pair making the particular response more likely to occur again.

A somewhat different theory has been formulated by Tolman[35] who attempts to deal with the *goal-directed whole acts* of the organism. The organism learns *connective* relationships and the *expectation* or probability of one stimulus following another. Learning is not the development of responses or habits, but of *expectancies,* which may be acted on in a variety of ways depending on the cumulative past experiences of the organism with the objects and the situations in its present environment. Reward and motivation affect performance, but have no direct effect upon learning. The theories of Hull and Tolman have been substantially combined by Osgood[24] as the *theory of mediational processes.*

Yet other approaches to the theory of learning are the *stochastic* (from the Greek, meaning to guess or conjecture) models of Estes[13] and Bush-Mosteller.[7] Here learning is treated as a succession of events with a number of possible alternative actions which can be executed at each stage. Initially, the response by the organism to a particular stimulus is determined by a given probability distribution. Learning changes the initial distribution into that assembly of probabilities which will ensure a particular end action for a given set of initial conditions. Only the current distribution of probabilities affects the generation of actions, i.e., no consideration is given to past history.

None of the above theories meets with universal acceptance, and the study of learning mechanisms must be greatly refined before it can make positive contributions to the engineering world. Unfortunately the subject is quite obtuse, without any of the usual conveniences of a generally accepted means of measurement, absolute references, or easy calibration. In contrast, our knowledge of the physical and chemical mechanisms of the nervous system appears quite substantial. This is probably due to the similarity between the neural structures of man and other living organisms, which allows a great deal of investigation to be conducted on more convenient animal cells. In investigations of the learning processes, this similarity is not particularly helpful since animals are quite limited in their learning ability and a natural communication problem exists. Furthermore, the subject must be maintained in an alert condition; this is not necessary for many physiological studies.

## THE NERVOUS SYSTEM*

The complexity of the human nervous system makes it impossible to describe in any simple fashion or to construct a realistic analog. In the first

---

*For more extensive information, consult the published works of J. C. Eccles, D. A. Sholl and S. S. Stevens. (See references 12, 32, and 34 at the end of this chapter).

place, the number of active elements is exceedingly large—far, far greater than the number presently evisaged for even the largest computing complex; second, the detailed interconnections of the active elements are unknown.

The basic structural unit in the nervous system, the neuron, is a single cell which has a central nucleus surrounded by protoplasm and enclosed in a thin tissue membrane. The neuron is excited by signals transmitted by many short, highly branched fibers known as *dendrites*. The signal speed is relatively slow, and the signals are attenuated during transmission. If there is sufficient energy from a single stimulated dendrite, or if a number of dendrites is stimulated at about the same time, the neuron will fire, generating a short-duration pulse which propagates without gross attenuation along the *axon*.

A schematic diagram of the interaction of two neurons is shown in Fig. 1–1. The degree of approximation in this diagram will be readily apparent if the reader will examine actual photographs of sectioned tissue.[4,5] Much of our knowledge of the human nervous system is based on experi-

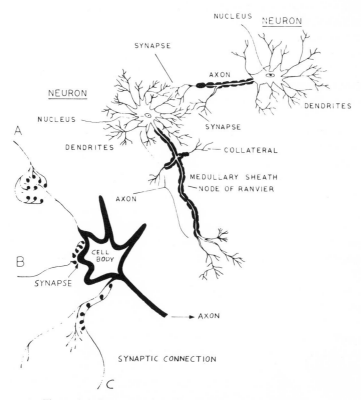

Figure 1–1 Representation of interaction of two neurons.

mental investigations of the nervous systems of animals, particularly the giant squid and the cockroach.

The pulse is transmitted along the axon at a speed of several meters per second (5 meters per second for fine axons; up to 125 meters per second for large axons) by an ionic process involving the interchange of sodium and potassium ions between the solution contained with the axon (*axoplasm*) and the solution external to the containing membrane (*blood dialysate*). The propagation of the impulse appears to depend on a relatively hard, impervious, segmented covering called the *medullary sheath*. The segments are separated from each other by small spaces known as *nodes of Ranvier*, which allow ionic exchange between the chemical solutions. The pulse energy is derived from the chemical mechanism triggered as the disturbance propagates, so that, should an impulse be weakened at one point by chemical contamination, its energy is restored as soon as it passes beyond this point. The magnitude of the impulse depends not on the original energy but on the energy available in each section of the fiber.[29]

Neurons can be divided roughtly on the basis of size and function. The peripheral nerves and pathways of the central nervous system are made up of *long-conducting* neurons, which are characterized by long single axons and long dendrites. Interconnections and alternate pathways are provided by *correlating* neurons, which are characterized by short dendrites and are only found within the central nervous system. The axon terminates in end brushes which lie close to the dendrites and cell walls of many other neurons, forming *synapses*.[14] The interaction is chemical and there is no fusion of the axon brush endings with the dendrites. Instead, the axon pulse liberates ions at the synaptic boundary, which diffuse in approximately one millisecond to the dendrite surface, changing the character of the nervous impulse from a narrow spike to a low potential signal which decays slowly.

Stylized examples of possible arrangements of synaptic connections are included in Fig. 1–1. Example *A* shows the interaction of the axon brush with localized dendrites, in which connection is made at some distance from the cell body. The signal crosses the synapses, and its various components travel approximately in phase towards the cell body. Example *B* shows the termination of the axon brush in synaptic junctions on the cell body itself. Because of the relatively high speed of axon transmissions, these signals also remain approximately in phase. Example *C* shows synaptic junctions which extend along a finite segment of a dendrite. In this case the signals entering the dendrite will be out of phase and may approximate a train on arrival at the cell body. Connections such as these may play a great part in neuron processing,[15] and the general problem of the interaction of spatial and spatiotemporal patterns in the axon brush-synapse-dendrite are being studied by a number of workers.[26]

Besides modifying the nature of the neural impulse, the synapse prevents the spread of nervous energy in all directions and serves to channel the information to, say, a limited number of effector organs so as to produce coordinated activity in a particular part of the body. The presence of the synapse differentiates the nervous systems of higher order organisms from lower order organisms. Some synaptic junctions have been found to produce excitatory or inhibitory action depending on the local signal environment, although such behavior appears to be rare.

Through the complex brushlike endings of the axon-synapse-dendrite network, a particular neuron may be connected to as few as one other neuron, or to as many as 1,000.[9] In the latter case, this may represent some 25,000 synaptic junctions.

Each stimulated dendrite transmits a low potential signal which is summed in some manner within the neuron so that, when the total excitation exceeds the firing threshold, an impulse is generated and propagates along the axon. The quiescent stimulation threshold level appears to depend on the size of the neuron (being lower for large cells) and on its immediate history; it may also depend on the neuron's long-term history. As soon as the neuron fires, a *refractory* period follows during which it is completely unresponsive to any stimulus; in a short time (up to 10 milliseconds) this gives way to a *partially refractory* period which may last up to 100 milliseconds, during which the threshold returns to its quiescent level. Figure 1–2 illustrates the elementary principles of neuron excitation. The reader should remember that models constructed as an aid to the interpretation of experimental results are strictly tools and that their apparent ability to explain extant phenomena is no guarantee of their physical existence.

Six *axon signals* and their corresponding dendrite signals are shown in stylized form in the figure. The total excitation applied to the neuron at any instant is assumed to be the sum of the instantaneous dendrite signals. With the quiescent value of the stimulation threshold as shown, the neuron will fire at point (*a*), generating an output pulse. The firing threshold immediately jumps to a large value and then decays to the quiescent level again. A second impulse is generated at (*b*). No impulse is generated at (*c*), even though the total excitation is above the quiescent level, since the neuron has just fired and is in the partially refractory period. Firing occurs again at (*d*) since the firing threshold has just fallen to the quiescent value, and at (*e*) the total excitation is sufficient to fire the neuron even though it is partially refractory. Normal firing occurs again at (*f*).

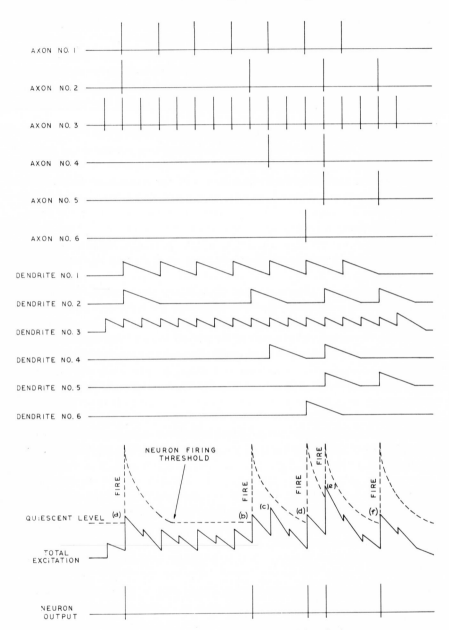

Figure 1-2 Illustration of neuronal functioning.

The refractory and partially refractory phases cause considerable modification of the neural impulse trains applied to a neuron. Examination of the regularity of actual nerve impulse trains shows that peripheral nerve fibers which have few interconnections respond to stimulation with nervous activity having somewhat regular pulse repetition intervals, while in the more central regions of the nervous system where many interconnections occur, the pulse trains may be quite irregular, with variations of as much as 100:1 in the pulse-to-pulse interval.

It must be recognized that this description is very elementary and ignores much of the major detail. For instance, it is almost axiomatic that the behavior of any living cell includes a random component or statistical fluctuation due to the very nature of the ionic processes which control its characteristics. Thus there will be variations in the threshold level for no apparent reason, and the response of a specific neuron to a given set of input signals will not always be the same. Conversely, apparently similar neurons will not necessarily behave in the same manner when subject to a similar environment.

A more serious problem is posed by behavior which appears to undermine the basic concept of the neuron as a threshold device. For instance, the response may sometimes depend on the sequence in which stimuli are applied, rather than on the value of the stimuli themselves, and the spatial patterns of the synaptic junctions make a complex input channel.

## THE SENSORY ORGANS

The sense organs contain *receptors* and the motor organs contain *effectors* both of which perform specialized tasks. They are connected to the neurons of the nervous system by synaptic junctions, and may be regarded as variations of the basic neuron to accommodate the input-output interface requirements. When a sustained physical stimulus is applied to a sense organ, some of the nerve fibers may respond with a brief burst of impulses which rapidly decrease in frequency and are not sustained for the duration of the stimulus. This phenomenon is termed *adaptation*. It probably serves to reduce the enormous amount of data transmitted to the central nervous system and prevents any one stimulus from capturing more than its share of attention.

Other fibers have been observed to respond to the cessation of a stimulus, and pairs of fibers have been found in which one generates a short burst of pulses at the onset of a stimulus and the other generates a burst of pulses when stimulation ceases. In the case of a physical stimulus which is applied to a large number of nerve fibers at the same time, lateral inhibition may occur, in which each fiber tends to inhibit the pulse trains generated by its neighbors. The degree of influence of a particular fiber appears to be related to the number of pulses being generated by the fiber itself. This type of behavior has been observed in some detail in the lateral eye of the horseshoe crab (limulus).[28]

In nature, extremely complex sensors perform the initial task of transforming environmental energy into neural energy. The human eye, for instance, contains a retina with some $10^8$ nerve endings in the form of *rods* and *cones,* which respond to light of various frequencies which is focused on them by an inorganic lens. An iris automatically adjusts the level of the incident energy. Normal sight apparently depends on minute oscillations of the eyeball which continuously perturb the position of the visual image on the retina, providing a dynamic signal input even though the environment is static.[25]

A schematic diagram of the major components of the visual system is shown in Fig. 1-3. The photoreceptor neurons (rods and cones) are connected to two other layers of neurons before the optic nerve carries the image data to the brain. The synaptic fields between the neuron layers serve to interconnect elements at the same level as well as contiguous levels and apparently perform specific image-processing functions. It is estimated that there may be more than 100 distinguishable kinds of network, each of which operates on some facet of the signal. Substantial preprocessing is believed to occur before the nervous activity describing the image reaches the brain.[36]

This belief is supported by the work of Lettvin et al. on the visual system of the frog,[20] in which they found groups of fibers performing separate functions. Thus, one group is sensitive to boundaries in the visual field such as are formed by two shades of gray. The response depends on the sharpness of the boundary and whether it moves; degree of contrast and light intensity appear to have no effect. Another group is sensitive to curved boundaries, provided the convex side is the darker and the boundary has moved recently. A third group of fibers responds to a moving silhouette. A fourth group is sensitive to general dimming of the receptive field, and a fifth group apparently produces signals which are related to the average level of illumination.

Using all of these networks, a frog is able to detect moving insects of a certain general size, which it will attack, and larger moving objects, which will cause it to flee. While the organization of the visual pathway is somewhat different from that of man, there is no reason to believe that the frog is unique in possessing some form of preprocessing.

As for the ear, it comprises an extremely delicate series of cavities shut off from the atmosphere by a sensitive membrane and connected to an

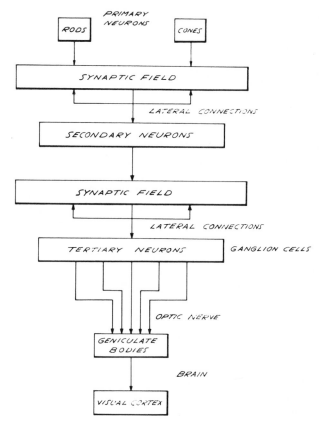

Figure 1-3 Representation of retinal layers and visual system.

intricately shaped member—the cochlea—which forms a resonant complex and reduces audio frequencies to the localized excitation of nerve endings. Phase differences between the energy received in the two ears provide stereophonic information,[8] which is used to determine the direction of a particular disturbance.

The human ear is orders of magnitude less complex than the eye.[37,38,39] Nevertheless it manages to capture the compressive waves which impinge on the ear cavity and to reduce them to data which, after processing by the brain, are recognized as a spoken word or other audible signal. The key to this data reduction is apparently the *cochlea*, a spiral tube which is filled with fluid (*perilymph*), shown in stylized section in Fig. 1-4. It is divided into three sections by two membranes running almost the full length of the tube. The center section (*scala media*) contains the *organ of Corti* which

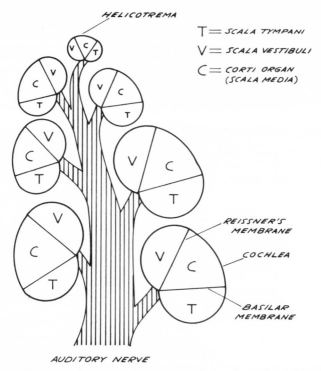

Figure 1-4 Diagrammatic representation of section through cochlea.

consists of 25,000–30,000 sensory nerve cells which connect to the auditory nerve. The two outer sections (*scala vestibuli, scala tympani*) form canals, which are connected at the extreme end of the cochlea (*helicotrema*) and which are stimulated by the sounds impinging on the ear. The liquid columns so formed have different mechanical characteristics so that the sound wave components travel at different speeds towards the helicotrema. This imbalance produces a nonuniform pressure field which excites the nerve cells of the organ of Corti. Maximum excitation is believed to be produced at points which correspond to maximum compression in the scala vestibuli and a simultaneous maximum rarefaction in the scala tympani.

The cochlea acts as a mechanical analyzer in which the position of maximum activity changes with frequency. At high frequencies (over 2,000 cycles per second) the frequency data is believed to be derived solely from the position of the excitation. At lower frequencies, the nerve cells are able to follow individual sound waves and the nerve impulses form *volleys*. Loudness is apparently measured by the number of sensor cells excited (they are split into two levels, probably with different thresholds) and, at the lower frequencies, by the length of the portion of the organ of Corti which is excited. Thus the recognition of speech and other sounds is achieved through a frequency- and amplitude-dependent analyzer which selectively excites components of the auditory nerve. Unfortunately, little is known of the subsequent processing of the sensor signals in the central nervous system.

The tongue comprises a large number of receptors which are individually sensitive to substances from one or more chemical classifications. Discrimination depends on the characteristic pattern established by a large number of these units. A similar mechanism may account for the sense of smell. The sense of touch is due to pressure-sensitive receptors located close to the surface of the skin.

Heat and cold are believed to be measured by separate networks of nerve endings, and many of the characteristics of living systems, such as ionic balance and body temperature, are believed to be maintained constant on the basis of balancing the activity of opposing systems of receptors, one being excited in proportion, and the other being excited in inverse proportion, to the magnitude of the effect.[10]

The brain is served by an estimated $10^8$ sensory nerve fibers. Computing the *maximum* data rate per fiber as $10^3$ bits per second on the basis of signal velocity, the *maximum* possible input data rate would be $10^{11}$ bits per second. (Barlow arrives at a lower figure of $3 \times 10^9$ bits per second on the basis of $3 \times 10^6$ sensory fibers.[3]) The average data rate per fiber, as estimated by Jacobsen,[18,19] is likely to range between 0.3 (estimated for the auditory channels) and 5 bits per second (estimated for the visual channels), giving $10^8$ bits per second as a realistic, average input rate. Jacobsen's estimates do not take second order effects into account (such as binaural effects, stereoscopic effects, and color perception).

The average human brain is estimated to consist of some $10^{10}$ neurons, of which about 1 percent are believed to be totally concerned with vision and 60 percent are believed to be partially involved. At the retina, some $10^8$ sensory elements connect to $10^6$ nerve fibers, which then increase in number before they terminate in the cerebral cortex.[21]

## ORGANIZATION

It is now generally accepted that the design for the basic structure of the nervous system (and of the body as a whole) is contained within the complex chemical materials which form the genes.[11] The major constituent is *deoxyribonucleic acid* (DNA) which forms large molecules several microns long. Structurally, the DNA molecule comprises a double spiral of alternate sugar and phosphate groups, linked, in ladder fashion, by pairs of *nucleotides*. Four separate nucleotides have been identified; they form 4 distinct pairs (not 12 as might be expected if the pairing were unrestricted). The sequential ordering of the pairs along the spiral ladder structure apparently controls the generation of the specific types of amino acids present in the human body.

The code is read by starting from a fixed point and proceeding along the chain three pairs at a time. Assuming that there are at least $10^{12}$ connections within the nervous system, it is inconceivable that each is specified exactly by this structure. However, since human beings bear a considerable resemblance to each other in terms of intellectual faculties, body function, etc., the fundamental organization of the nervous system must be transmitted by this means. The detailed structure is probably developed at random and could vary greatly from individual to individual; in fact, chance organization in some of these areas *may* be the reason certain of us are more adept at electrical engineering than biology, and vice versa.

While patient investigators have been able to piece together data concerning the neuron and the gross properties of the nervous system, little is known of the functions of the physical parts of the brain. The best known facts concern the organization of the input and output pathways—the sensor and motor neurons. For instance, signals generated by auditory stimuli are believed to be received by the brain in areas ordered by pitch,[23] and tactile stimulus signal reception areas are believed to be ordered by gross bodily location. Similarly, the generating areas for the signals exciting motor neurons appear to be arranged in an order roughly corresponding to the location of the muscles and glands they control.

Other data show that flexibility must also exist. Thus, the destruction of part of the brain by a stroke or similar catastrophe may temporarily deprive the subject of motor skills or recall, but these functions are regained after a period of therapy, indicating that other areas of the brain have been able to assume the role of the destroyed tissue. Redundancy, therefore, is also a salient feature in the composition of the brain. That it exists is also supported by the observation that a man's intellectual capability lasts well into old age, despite the facts that regeneration of brain cells appears to cease soon after he becomes an adult, and that cell decay continues until the end of his life.[33]

## MEMORY

Although the human mind has an enormous capacity for the retention of facts, sensations, situations, motives, prejudices, and the like, no specific location has been identified as being exclusively associated with memory; indeed the consensus of opinion is that it is widely distributed throughout the brain. In some models, the storage mechanism is envisaged as recirculating loops broadly similar to the delay-line principle incorporated in some early digital computers,[27] while, in others, a less volatile mechanism is postulated, such as a structural or chemical change.[16]

Memory appears to be the indispensable attribute to learning; without it, prior events cannot be *recalled* for use in providing cues for the current situation. In neuron models, memory is simulated by adjusting the gain of the input connections so that certain functions are more likely to be computed; setting a threshold level; or adjusting other technical features. In the living system, no such specific mechanism has been identified. Among many theories,[24] one hypothesis is the concept of *memory trace* in which the occurrence of a given training pattern is postulated to cause certain pathways within the brain mass to become more likely to conduct than others, so that, upon the recurrence of the stimulus (or one closely associated with it), the same pathways are likely to be activated and thus form the same output. The trace is subject to decay, and, if it is not reinforced for some time, the probability of forming the proper response upon application of the stimulus decreases.

The memory trace associated with any particular input-output relationship includes all of those modifiable characteristics throughout the nervous system which make the repetitive formation of the connective possible. Each trace represents a portion of the brain's total storage capacity. Since it is to be expected that corresponding connectives may be formed for similar input-output relationships, portions of a particular trace may be shared in common with other traces, and the occurrence of a particular event may not only regenerate its specific trace but also regenerate the common portions of similar traces. In this way, cognizance of a particular event is maintained even though it may not recur for a long time. In fact, groups of closely related phenomena can be regarded as giving rise to *trace systems* in which there is a degree of commonality and intermixing of the individual components.

If we assume that the elements comprising the trace are binary, that they are *noisy* (in the communications sense), that some of the elements are redundant, and that information is coded in an optimum fashion, the mechanism is susceptible to restricted analysis[6] using communication theory.[30,31] If the probability of a particular element making an error is $P$, the general relation between the average element information capacity and error probability is shown in Fig. 1–5.

Where redundancy exists and optimum coding (finite) can be achieved, the reliability at lower error probabilities improves (see figure). In fact, if sufficient redundancy is available, the trace information can be retained

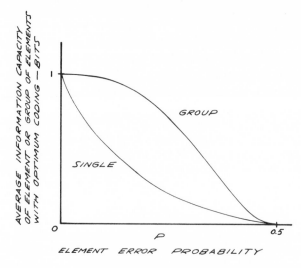

Figure 1–5 Information capacity of storage trace element.

under any reasonable value of *P*. However, since the brain is finite, and even the simple acts in life require the activation of a large number of neurons, it is apparent that the degree of redundancy afforded any particular connective must be seriously limited. Furthermore, it seems likely that the degree of redundancy assigned to a given trace must vary in proportion to its importance (as judged by the organism). Otherwise all data would be equally likely to decay and fall below the level of recall.

It is certainly true that lessons learned early in life or during highly stressed or catastrophic situations are those best remembered. In the case of early learning, a higher level of redundancy may be responsible, since the cumulative amount of information stored is small compared to the ultimate capacity of the system. In stressed situations, the lesson has an urgency which may give more priority to the connective with a resulting greater level of redundancy, perhaps at the expense of traces already formed.

## DISCUSSION

The painstaking work of a large number of investigators has contributed to unraveling some of the mysteries of the nervous system. The reader will readily appreciate that the duplication of a complex with $10^{10}$ active elements is beyond our present capability, for, even if components were available and the structure was known, the basic economics of size, expense, and power consumption would be prohibitive. Thus, even an active element density of 1,000,000 per cubic foot gives a total volume of 10,000 cubic feet (i.e., assuming a standard relay rack contains approximately 10 cubic feet of usable space, this would require 1,000 such racks). Using conventional equipment installation spacing, these racks would require some 16,000 square feet of floor space. Since the best practical component densities are little more than 1,000,000 per cubic foot, an estimate which more closely reflects present capabilities might be 100,000 square feet (assuming some 10 components per active element). A conservative cost estimate would run into billions of dollars. As for power consumption, at 1 milliwatt per active element, the total would be 10 megawatts.

Further reflection leads to yet other problems; if the active elements could be made continuously at a rate of 1,000 per minute, it would require some 16 years to fabricate the total complement. It is evident that the useful life of the majority would be over before the production run was complete. So we have a practical restriction to our topic. Within the context of this book, a few neuronlike devices acting in concert towards some common goal will be considered to constitute an intelligent machine.

The discussion of the approaches to machine intelligence which follows is divided into two parts: Part I describes the properties of the major neuron models and discusses the characteristics of simple learning systems; Part II describes the application of some of these principles to pattern recognition, computer programming, and reliable networks.

## REFERENCES

1. A. W. Andrew, "Learning in a Non-Digital Environment," *Aspects of the Theory of Artificial Intelligence,* C. A. Muses, ed., Plenum Press, New York, 1962, pp. 1–7.
2. W. R. Ashby, "Principles of the Self-Organizing System," *Principles of Self-Organization,* H. von Foerster and G. W. Zopf, eds., Pergamon Press, New York, 1962, pp. 255–278.
3. H. B. Barlow, "Sensory Mechanisms, the Reduction of Redundancy, and Intelligence," *Mechanization of Thought Processes,* Her Majesty's Stationery Office, London, 1959, vol. 2, pp. 535–574.
4. R. L. Buerle, "Storage and Manipulation of Information in the Brain," *Journal, Institution of Electrical Engineers,* vol. 5, 1959, pp. 75–82.
5. D. Bodian and N. Taylor, "Synapse Arising at Central Node of Ranvier, and Note on Fixation of Central Nervous System," *Science,* vol. 139, 1963, pp. 330–332.
6. J. Brown, "Information, Redundancy, and Decay of the Memory Trace," *Mechanization of Thought Processes,* Her Majesty's Stationery Office, London, 1959, vol. 2, pp. 731–745.

7. F. R. Bush and R. Mosteller, *Stochastic Models for Learning,* John Wiley, New York, 1955.

8. C. Cherry, "Two Ears—but One World," *Sensory Communication,* W. A. Rosenblith, ed., MIT Press and John Wiley, New York, 1961, pp. 99–117.

9. W. E. LeG. Clark, "Central Nervous System," *Textbook of Human Anatomy,* W. J. Hamilton, ed., Macmillan, New York, 1956, pp. 689–818.

10. M. J. Cohen, "Peripheral Organization of Sensory Systems," *Neuron Theory and Modeling,* R. F. Reiss, ed., Stanford University Press, Stanford, Calif., 1964, pp. 273–292.

11. Francis Crick, "The Genetic Code," *Scientific American,* vol. 207, October 1962, pp. 66–74.

12. J. C. Eccles, *The Neurophysiological Basis of Mind,* Oxford University Press, London, 1953.

13. W. K. Estes, "Toward a Statistical Theory of Learning," *Psychological Review,* vol. 57, 1950, pp. 94–107.

14. L. D. Harmon, "Natural and Artificial Synapses," *Self-Organizing Systems—1962,* M. C. Yovitts, G. T. Jacobi, and G. D. Goldstein, eds., Spartan Books, Washington, D.C., 1962, pp. 177–202.

15. ———, "Problems in Neural Modeling," *Neural Theory and Modeling,* R. F. Reiss, ed., Stanford University Press, Stanford, Calif., 1964, pp. 9–30.

16. D. O. Hebb, *The Organization of Behavior,* John Wiley, New York, 1949.

17. C. L. Hull, *Principles of Behavior,* Appleton-Century-Crofts, New York, 1943.

18. H. Jacobsen, "The Information Capacity of the Human Ear," *Science,* vol. 112, 1950, p. 143.

19. ———, "Information Capacity of the Human Eye," *Science,* vol. 113, 1950, p. 292.

20. J. Y. Lettvin, H. Maturana, W. S. McCulloch, and W. Pitts, "What the Frog's Eye Tells the Frog's Brain," *Proceedings, IRE,* vol. 47, 1959, pp. 1940–1951.

21. W. S. McCulloch, M. A. Arbib, and J. Cowan, "Neurological Models and Integrative Procedures," *Self-Organizing Systems—1962,* M. C. Yovitts, G. T. Jacobi, and G. D. Goldstein, eds., Spartan Books, Washington, D.C., 1962, pp. 49–60.

22. M. B. Mitchell, "Progress Report on Bionics—Aeronautical Systems Division," *Proceedings, National Aerospace Electronics Conference, (NAECON),* 1962, pp. 496–498.

23. W. D. Neff, "Neural Mechanism of Auditory Discrimination," *Sens-*

*ory Communication,* W. A. Rosenblith, ed., MIT Press and John Wiley, New York, 1961, pp. 259–278.

24. C. E. Osgood, *Method and Theory in Experimental Psychology,* Oxford University Press, London, 1953.

25. R. M. Pritchard, "Stabilized Retinal Images and Visual Perception," *Biological Prototypes and Synthetic Systems,* E. E. Bernard and M. R. Kare, eds., Plenum Press, New York, 1962, vol. 1, pp. 119–125.

26. W. Rall, "Dendritic Trees and Neuronal Input-Output Relations," *Neural Theory and Modeling,* R. F. Reiss, ed., Stanford University Press, Stanford, Calif., 1964, pp. 73–97.

27. N. Rashevsky, *Mathematical Biophysics,* Dover Publications, New York, 1960 (3rd. rev. ed.), Chap. 18.

28. F. Ratliff, "Inhibitory Interaction and the Detection of Enhancement of Contours," *Sensory Communication,* W. A. Rosenblith, ed., MIT Press and John Wiley, New York, 1961, pp. 183–203.

29. W. A. H. Rushton, "Peripheral Coding in the Nervous System," *ibid.,* pp. 169–181.

30. C. E. Shannon, "A Mathematical Theory of Communication," *Bell System Technical Journal,* vol. 27, 1948, pp. 379–423.

31. _____ and W. Weaver, *The Mathematical Theory of Communication,* University of Illinois Press, Urbana, Ill., 1949.

32. D. A. Sholl, *The Organization of The Cerebral Cortex,* Methuen, London, 1956.

33. R. W. Sperry, "Orderly Function with Disordered Structure," *Principles of Self-Organization,* H. von Foerster and G. W. Zopf, eds., Pergamon Press, New York, 1962, pp. 279–290.

34. S. S. Stevens, ed., *Handbook of Experimental Psychology,* John Wiley, New York, 1951.

35. E. C. Tolman, *Purposive Behavior in Animals and Man,* Appleton-Century-Crofts, New York, 1932.

36. S. Polyak, *The Vertebrate Visual System,* University of Chicago Press, Chicago, 1957.

37. H. Davis, "Peripheral Coding of Auditory Information," *Sensory Communication,* W. A. Rosenblith, ed., MIT Press and John Wiley, New York, 1961, pp. 119–141.

38. L. A. de Rosa, and L. M. Vallese, "Nature's Contribution to Correlation Processes," *Bionics Symposium,* WADD Technical Report 60-600, 1960, pp. 339–353.

39. W. F. Caldwell, E. Glaesser, and J. L. Stewart, "Design of an Analog Ear," *Biological Prototypes and Synthetic Systems,* E. E. Barnard and M. R. Kare, eds., Plenum Press, New York, 1962, vol. 1, pp. 97–103.

# PART I
# MODELS

Chapter 2

# NEURON MODELS

A valid approach to the problem of understanding and using the principles of human intelligence is to study or build devices patterned after theoretical models of a neuron. This should be done not only to establish a building block which can be interconnected in networks, and which may eventually perform useful tasks, but also to express the basic properties of the models in engineering terms, to isolate those characteristics which control the behavior of the individual simulated neurons (and simple interconnections), and to develop a working knowledge of the functions which can be performed by these devices. This is part of the analysis which must occur before synthesis can take place, and goes hand-in-hand with the design of the overall system. Unfortunately, the processes occurring within the neuron are still little understood and, perhaps because of this, appear to be unduly complex.

Neuron models may be classified on the basis of the mode of implementation (i.e., chemical, electronic, computer simulation, or theoretical) or the extent of the imitation (i.e., partial unit, single unit, or network). Using such descriptors, L. D. Harmon has identified some 50 representative approaches.[18] In this chapter the more important attempts at neuron modeling and quasi-modeling will be described. The techniques have been selected on the basis of historical significance, practical application to learning systems, or potential for development.

## FORMAL NEURON

Historically, perhaps the most important attempt to devise a neuromine is the *formal neuron* of McCulloch and Pitts, developed in the early 1940's.[28] Since the appearance of their original paper,[25] the concept has been refined and extended. Our discussion is based on recent presentations by McCulloch[26] and Blum.[4,5]

A formal neuron is a device with *n* inputs and one output. Each input and the single output are binary in nature. The input signals may be 0 (OFF) or 1 (ON, excitatory, or inhibitory). Connections from a specific

27

input may divide, but cannot combine with other inputs.  The device is unidirectional, with signals passing from input to output.  A time delay occurs between the application of an input signal and the appearance of an output signal (if any).  The neuron fires when the instantaneous arithmetic sum of excitatory and inhibitory input signals exceeds a given threshold.  Immediately after firing, it can be fired again by any combination of signals which equals or exceeds the threshold, i.e., refractory behavior is neglected.  A symbolic representation of a formal neuron is shown in Fig. 2-1.

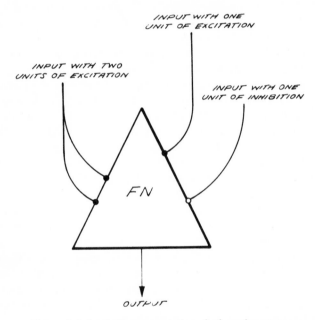

Figure 2-1 Symbolic representation of a formal neuron.

Venn diagrams[19] are commonly used to represent the functions which may be computed by such a device.  They have a long history[27] and are convenient to use once a few elementary properties have been learned.  Consider a set of events $A$ represented by the symbolic closed curve as shown in Fig. 2-2.  The area outside the curve represents all other events which are $\overline{A}$ (not $A$).  Now consider a set of events $B$ which includes some of $A$.  The interrelation can be represented by the looped curves shown in Fig. 2-3.  The common area represents coincidence of events, i.e., $A.B$ ($A$ and $B$).  The remaining areas within the two closed curves represent a set of one events and not the other ($A.\overline{B}$, $\overline{A}.B$), while the area outside of the two curves represents neither set of events ($\overline{A}.\overline{B}$.).  Three overlapping sets of events, $A$, $B$, and $C$, can be represented by the curves shown in Fig. 2-4.

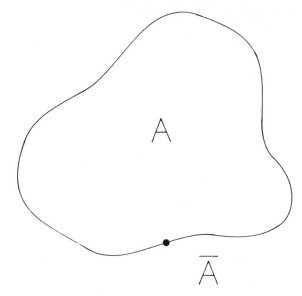

Figure 2–2 Representation of an event $A$.

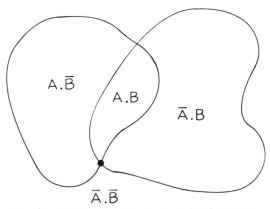

Figure 2–3 Representation of two overlapping events.

It will be observed that each segment corresponds to one of the minterms of the Boolean expansion of three functions. Instead of drawing the complete curves, a convenient shorthand can be introduced, as in the diagrams shown in Fig. 2–5. They are essentially stylized versions of Figs. 2–2, 2–3, and 2–4 in the vicinity of the large dots in each diagram. In normal use, the minterms are not written in, but their presence is indicated by a dot. Extension to more than three variables requires considerable artistic ability; suitable representations have been developed by Selfridge and Minsky.[4]

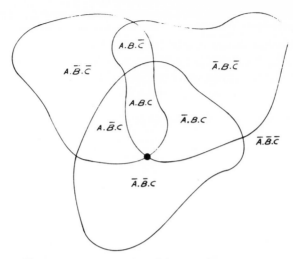

Figure 2-4 Representation of three overlapping events.

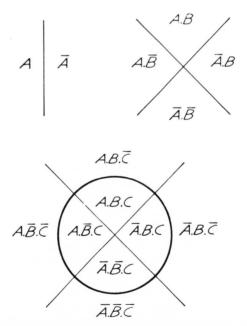

Figure 2-5 Venn diagram for one, two, and
three overlapping events.

Consider a formal neuron with three inputs *A, B,* and *C.* Let *A* provide two units of excitation, *B* one unit of negative excitation, and *C* one unit of excitation, as shown in Fig. 2–6. The logical functions which can be computed, i.e., which will fire the neuron, will depend on the threshold level $\theta$. If $\theta \geq 4$, the neuron will never fire; if $\theta \leq -1$, it will always fire.

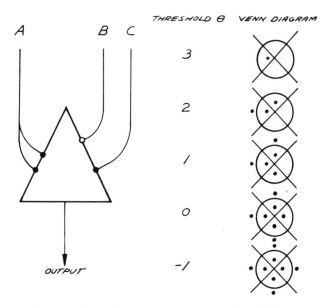

Figure 2–6 Venn diagram representation of logical functions which can be computed by a given 3-input formal neuron for various levels of threshold.

The computable functions for $4 > \theta \geq -1$ are shown in the Venn diagrams accompanying the figure. If the configuration of the neuron is changed, the relation of the computable functions to threshold is changed.

Besides direct application to the neuron itself, inhibition can be applied between inputs (*afferent* inhibition), as shown in Fig. 2–7. In this case excitation of *B* reduces the strength of *A* from 2 units to 1 unit. The variation of the computable functions with threshold is somewhat different from the performance of the neuron shown in Fig. 2–6.

A study of Figs. 2–6 and 2–7 shows the Venn diagram to be clumsy in describing the computing capability when there are many threshold levels. To abbreviate this, a single diagram can be drawn showing the numerical value of excitation which will first allow each input combination to be computed. Such threshold diagrams are shown in Fig. 2–8.

Taking the process yet one step further, it is possible to convert threshold diagrams into *sequence* diagrams which represent the order in which

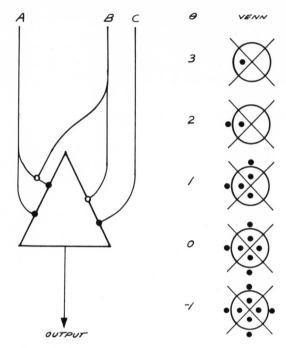

Figure 2-7 Three-input formal neuron with input inhibition.

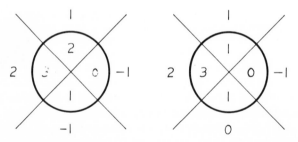

Figure 2-8 Composite excitation diagrams for formal neurons shown in Figs. 2-6 and 2-7 as Threshold Decreases.

the neuron fires as the threshold decreases, as shown in Fig. 2-9. Threshold diagrams can be distinguished from sequence diagrams by the appearance of a zero in the $\overline{A}.\overline{B}.\overline{C}.$ space of the threshold diagram. No zeros appear in the sequence diagram.

Lest the construction of formal neuron configurations appears to be a matter of chance, it should be noted that Blum provides an algorithm for constructing a neuron for any valid Venn diagram and provides a proof

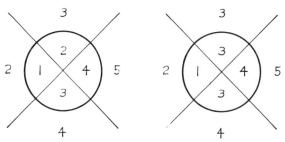

Figure 2-9 Sequence of computable functions for formal
neurons shown in Figs. 2-6 and 2-7 as Threshold Decreases.

for the existence of a neuron which will compute a given sequence of
logical functions as the threshold is varied, step by step.

Formal neurons have little interest as isolated units; certainly their
existence cannot be justified on the basis of exercises in the manipulation
of Venn diagrams. When connected together in networks, however, they
can be made to exhibit two important properties: (1) retention of logical
stability under a common shift of threshold and (2) reliable computation
of specific functions by networks of unreliable components.

The network of three formal neurons shown in Fig. 2–10 is an example
of a McCulloch net which will compute $A.B$ irrespective of common
changes of threshold of the individual neurons (within certain limits).[26]
Threshold diagrams are shown in the body of neurons 1 and 2. For
neuron 3, the threshold diagram will depend on the thresholds of neurons
1 and 2 (i.e., $\theta_1$ and $\theta_2$). Diagrams are shown for: $\theta_1 = -1$ and $\theta_2 = +1$; $\theta_1 = -2$ and $\theta_2 = 0$; $\theta_1 = -3$ and $\theta_2 = -1$. For sequential values
of $\theta_3 = 0, -1$, and $-2$, the output function is always $A.B$. Nets which can
compute the same function, despite simultaneous (or independent)
changes of individual thresholds, are known as *logically stable nets*.

It has been suggested by McCulloch that this property may provide a
clue to the manner in which (some) human beings are able to retain their
mental faculties even after consuming sufficient alcohol to produce a significant change in the makeup of the blood and, hence, to introduce con-
taminants in the nervous system which cause a change in the neuron firing
levels. Should the threshold level become so high that neuron activity
ceases, coma will ensue, while, if the threshold level drops so that the
neurons fire spontaneously, seizure occurs.

Certain errors can occur in formal neurons.[40,41] One is that the input or
output lines may be intermittent so that they fail to pass the required
pulse. In consonance with the biological equivalents, an error caused by
an intermittent input connection is referred to as a *synaptic* error, and an
error caused by an intermittent output connection is called an *axonal* er-

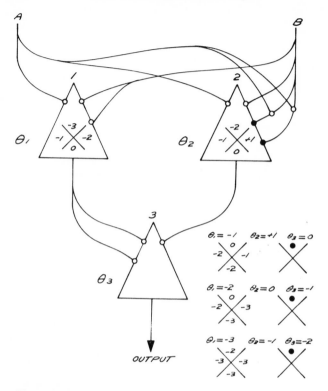

Figure 2-10 McCulloch network of formal neurons which compute the function $A.B.$ irrespective of common changes of threshold.

ror. These errors are normally indistinguishable for connections between neurons.

Another possible source of error may be variations in the amplitude of the input or output pulses of particular neurons. Since this is inconsistent with our description of the propagation of pulses along the axon, and also with the behavior of modern digital circuitry, it is not considered to be a major source of errors and will be ignored.

By choosing the proper connections, networks can be designed which will compute specific functions even though the individual neurons are subject to error. Fig. 2-11 shows a network of four neurons, each of which has a probability of computing certain functions other than that which is desired. A detailed inspection reveals that the overall computation will be the *exclusive-or* combination $A.\overline{B}.\overline{C} + \overline{A}.B.C$, irrespective of the false computation of the individual units.[46] The Venn diagram notation has been modified to include the symbol $P$ to indicate those functions which are subject to error.

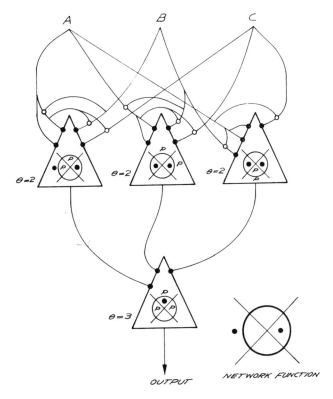

Figure 2-11 Reliable computation of a specific network function by formal neurons with statistical errors.

Thus the formal neuron model provides a glimpse of how neurons may
continue to perform their varied functions even though the state of the
human body may change or some of the neuron functions may become
disabled or intermittent. Among other things, it has led to the analysis of
redundant configurations and their use in ensuring the reliable performance of functions, even though a large percentage of the individual elements are defective.

## AUTOMATON

Standard results in Boolean algebra[19] give:

$$1.\ \overline{(a.b)} = \bar{a} + \bar{b}$$
$$\text{(Law of Duality)} \qquad (2.1)$$
$$2.\ \bar{a}.\bar{b} = \overline{(a + b)}$$

and

$$a = \overline{(\overline{a})} \qquad \text{(Law of Double Negation)} \qquad (2.2)$$

Hence

$$
\begin{aligned}
&1.\ a.b = \overline{(\overline{a} + \overline{b})}\\
&2.\ (a + b) = \overline{(\overline{a}.\overline{b})}
\end{aligned}
\qquad (2.3)
$$

so that any complex logical function can be implemented by a network of devices performing *and* and *negate* or *or* and *negate*. The former corresponds to Peirce's *arrow-function* and the latter corresponds to Sheffer's *stroke-function.*

Although the *formal neuron* was postulated to have a unit time delay between the application of a total excitation larger than the threshold and the appearance of an output pulse, no specific use has been made of this property in our presentation. By including a time delay of $p$ units, where $p$ may vary from element to element, von Neumann[43,44] developed a set of devices called *basic organs,* which perform the functions noted above (or variations of them) and which can be interconnected to form *automata* for the synthesis of complex logical functions. A specifiable number of unit time delays per organ is necessary to balance the responses of multilayer networks. As in the case of the formal neuron, certain network inputs are excitatory, certain are inhibitory, and the response of a given unit depends on the threshold level.

Automata can also be constructed from *majority organs,* i.e., elements which generate a response whenever more than half of their inputs are excited. In contrast, threshold elements generate a response only when enough inputs are excited to equal or exceed the threshold level. Figure 2–12 illustrates the different behavior of a 5-input device operated as a majority organ and as a threshold device. As a majority organ, it generates response when any three inputs are excited; as a threshold organ, the generation of an output depends on the value of the threshold level and the number of inputs excited. For an even number of inputs, it is usual to arrange that the majority element fires when $1 + n/2$ inputs are excited. Representing a majority organ as shown in Fig. 2–13A, Fig. 2–13B shows a majority organ which computes the *and*-function, and Fig. 2–13C shows a majority organ which forms the *or*-function. The inputs labeled 0 and 1 are permanently connected and form a bias which allows the functions to be formed.

The major significance of von Neumann's work lies in the reduction of large networks, which perform complex logical functions, into an assembly of elementary networks which can perform the same complex function. Thus it is possible to synthesize any complex function with a

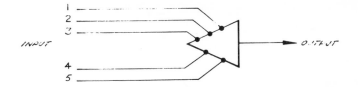

| INPUT | OUTPUT | | |
|---|---|---|---|
| | MAJORITY | THRESHOLD $\theta$ | |
| 1 0 1 1 0 | 1 | 1<br>2<br>3<br>4<br>5<br>6 | 1<br>1<br>1<br>0<br>0<br>0 |
| 1 0 0 0 0 | 0 | 1<br>2<br>3<br>4<br>5<br>6 | 1<br>0<br>0<br>0<br>0<br>0 |
| 1 1 1 1 0 | 1 | 1<br>2<br>3<br>4<br>5<br>6 | 1<br>1<br>1<br>1<br>0<br>0 |

Figure 2-12 Typical input-output combinations illustrating the difference between a majority element and a threshold element.

few repetitive building blocks, each of which is formed from an essentially simple element.

There is no direct evidence that these constructions appear in nature; indeed the existence of neurons with a very large number of inputs can be interpreted as providing contrary evidence. However, some processing of this kind might conceivably occur in the smaller neurons.

## ADAPTIVE LINEAR NEURON

A basic limitation of the formal neurons, and of the automata just described, is their inability to adapt their performance on the basis of signals from a goal network. While, for a given threshold, it is possible to com-

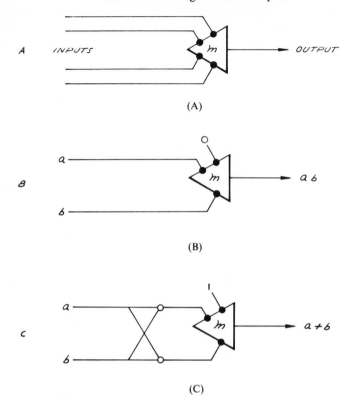

Figure 2-13 A—representation of a majority organ; B—*and-*function using a majority organ; C—*or-*function using a majority organ.

pute logical expressions, there is no way of changing the response so as to favor a desired function, or set of functions, once the input connections have been established. True, a fixed sequential variation is achieved by adjusting the threshold level, but there can be no change in the computable sequence.

It is essential that a learning device be able to give preference to one or more functions independently and to alter its behavior as time and conditions change. One way in which this may be done is to provide the device with the capability of adapting to the strengths of the input signals. Such a technique has been implemented by B. Widrow and others[45] in the *ada-line* (or *ada*ptive *line*ar) neuron.

A functional diagram of this device is shown in Fig. 2-14. Each input line includes an element with gain *a* (positive or negative) which can be varied as desired. The input and output signals are two-valued and are

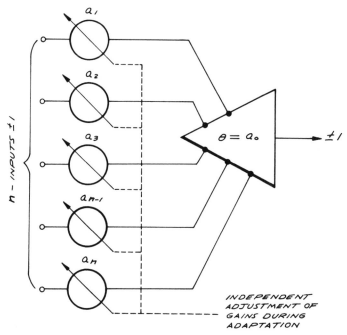

Figure 2–14 Basic adaline configuration.

normally designated $\pm 1$ rather than 1 and 0, since the symmetry introduced makes theoretical analysis somewhat easier. An output $(+1)$ occurs when:

$$a_1 x_1 + a_2 x_2 + \ldots a_n x_n \geq a_0, \tag{2.4}$$

where $x_1 x_2 \ldots x_n$ are binary functions and equal $\pm 1$ at all times. Besides the gain of the input channels, the threshold level $a_0$ is also adjustable. For fixed gain values, any combination of $x_1 x_2 \ldots x_n$ will produce one of the two possible outputs $(\pm 1)$. Thus the $2^n$ possible input combinations are classified into two sets (dichotomized). Variations of the individual signal gains (weights) and of the threshold level will change this division.

However, it is not possible to divide the signal space arbitrarily. Consider a 2-input $(A, B)/1$-output device; the four minterms $A.B$, $\bar{A}.B$, $A.\bar{B}$ and $\bar{A}.\bar{B}$ can be represented in function space as shown in Fig. 2–15. By adjusting the input weights and the threshold level, the functions can be separated into two classes. This is equivalent to the separation formed by the dotted straight line in the figure.[24] For this particular example, $A.\bar{B}$ is placed in one class $(+1,$ say) and the remaining functions are placed in the other class $(-1)$.

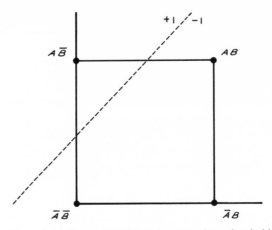

Figure 2–15 Separation of function space by a threshold
element.

By varying the slope and position of the line (training) the following
dichotomies can be made as shown in Fig. 2–16.

1. $A.\bar{B} \, / A.B \ \bar{A}.B \ \bar{A}.\bar{B}$          5. $\bar{A}.B \, / \bar{A}.\bar{B} \ A.\bar{B} \ A.B$

2. $A.\bar{B} \ \bar{A}.\bar{B} \, / A.B \ \bar{A}.B$          6. $\bar{A}.\bar{B} \, / \bar{A}.B. \ A.\bar{B} \ A.B$

3. $A.B \, / \bar{A}.B \ A.\bar{B} \ \bar{A}.\bar{B}$          7. $A.B \ \bar{A}.B \ A.\bar{B} \ \bar{A}.\bar{B} \, /$

4. $A.\bar{B} \ A.B. \, / \bar{A}.B \ \bar{A}.\bar{B}$

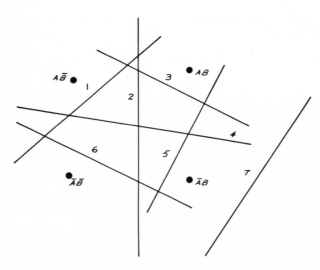

Figure 2–16 Separation of function space by a trainable
threshold element.

Since each section may be assigned $\pm 1$ depending on the training, this represents 14 functions which can be computed.

The total number of distinct combinations for two inputs is $2^2$, or 4, and the total number of distinct input-output functions which can be formed (computed) by a 2-input/1-output device is $2^{2^2}$, or 16. There are, thus, two functions which cannot be separated by a 2-input threshold element. Inspection of the diagram shows that these are: *exclusive-or* $(A.\bar{B}. + \bar{A}.B)$, and *contradiction* $(A.B + \overline{A.B})$. The 14 functions which can be differentiated are known as *linear separable* functions. They are the *only* functions which can be computed.

As the number of inputs increases, the number of linear separable functions decreases as a fraction of the total possible functions. While no explicit expression exists for computing this relationship, specific values have been derived, as follows:[7,22]

| No. of Inputs ($n$) | Maximum Possible Computable Functions ($2^{2^n}$) | No. of Functions Computable by Threshold Device | Percent of Total Realized |
|---|---|---|---|
| 1 | 4 | 4 | 100% |
| 2 | 16 | 14 | 80 |
| 3 | 256 | 104 | 41 |
| 4 | 65,536 | 1882 | 2.9 |

As the number of inputs increases, the total number of computable functions, as a percentage of all possible functions, becomes vanishingly small.[33] However, since the number of possible functions increases as the double exponent, the number of computable functions is still a moderately large number.

During training, an analog indicator is used with adaline to measure the magnitude of the total signal applied to the threshold device, so that, by comparison with the desired level, a measure of gross error can be obtained. This error is then reduced by progressive adjustment of the gains $a_1, a_2, \ldots$ etc., until the proper output is achieved. The functions to be learned are presented in sequence, with the sequence being repeated again and again, as often as possible, until all of the inputs have been learned. As discussed above, not all combinations of input-output signals are logically separable and so cannot be uniquely learned.

The problem of whether a particular training procedure can guarantee convergence to a solution has stimulated a great deal of theoretical analysis directed towards particular models. One of the more general expositions has been given by A. Novikoff, who shows that, provided the desired classification is possible (linear separable functions), rote presentation of the input stimuli, together with sequential adjustment of the input weights, can adjust the element performance so that the desired classification can be made.[32]

Adalines can be interconnected in parallel fashion to form $n$-input/$m$-output devices as shown in Fig. 2–17. Each adaline has $n$-input connections and 1 output, and there are $m$ such adalines in the network. By adding a majority gate or other fixed logic element which combines the outputs into one, the learning capacity of the network can be greatly in-

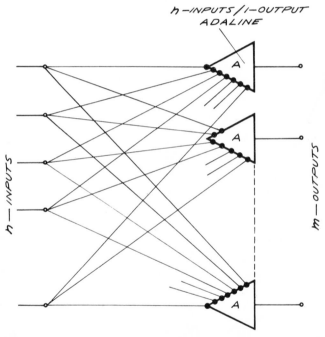

Figure 2-17 Parallel interconnection of adalines to make $n$-input/$m$-output network.

creased over that of a single $n$-input/1-output adaline. The multiple *adaline* configuration is usually referred to as a *madaline* network.

Besides simple parallel interconnections, some work is also being devoted to the investigation of the properties of multilayer networks, i.e., one layer of parallel, interconnected adalines feeding another layer of parallel, interconnected adalines. As might be expected, the selection of an appropriate convergent training procedure requires a great deal of care. Despite their complexity, or perhaps because of it, such networks appear to exhibit a generalization capability, i.e., the ability to respond satisfactorily to input signals of the same general nature as the training signals.

In order to implement the adaline simply and cheaply, Widrow and Hoff[45] have devised an electrochemical component called a *memistor* (res*istor* with a *memo*ry), which possesses variable gain characteristics. It comprises a small electrolytic cell containing two electrodes immersed in a plating solution. Typically, one electrode might be a carbon rod and the other a copper wire. The resistance of the combination can be changed by plating copper onto the carbon cathode. Elements have been made with a high degree of reproducibility, in which the terminal resistance can be changed from 50 ohms to 2 ohms in about 5 seconds with a fraction of a milliampere current. Adaptation is achieved by the application of direct current to the memistor cell. So as not to destroy the state of the individual memistors, the input signals are alternating currents and the signal value is associated with the phase of the current.

## PERCEPTRON*

The term *perceptron* describes a class of theoretical nerve networks which are said to model the gross properties of the brain (in a restricted sense), and which include sensor and effector (motor) neurons. These devices have been developed by F. Rosenblatt and his colleagues at Cornell Aeronautical Laboratory. Through usage, the term perceptron, when spelled with a capital "P" (Perceptron), signifies specific hardware built at Cornell.[2,3] It is, however, used as a generic term denoting various nerve network constructions whose major purpose is to assist in the investigation of possible network structures and theoretical processing principles which might shed light on the development of intelligence. A perceptron comprises *sensory*-units, *association*-units, and *response*-units.

A *sensory unit*, or *S-unit*, responds to environmental changes so as to emit a signal which is in some way associated with the magnitude of the change. Using Rosenblatt's notation, the output of an S-unit, $s_i$, excited by an input signal $c_{wi}^*(t)$ from an environment $w$, is $s_i^*(t)$.

If

$$s_i^* = +1, \text{ when } c_{wi}^* > \theta_i \text{ (threshold)}, \qquad (2.5)$$

*This section is based largely on the work of F. Rosenblatt (see reference 35 at the end of this chapter).

and

$$s_i^* = 0, \text{ when } c_{wi} \leq \theta_i, \tag{2.6}$$

the unit is a threshold device and is termed a *simple S-unit.*

An *association unit,* or *A-unit,* is a logical-decision, signal-generating device. The output of an A-unit, $a_j$, excited by a sequence of input signals $c_{ij}^*(t)$, is $a_j^*(t)$. The input signals $c_{ij}^*(t)$ are those transmitted from S-unit $s_i$ to A-unit $a_j$ by connection $c_{ij}$. The relation between $s_i^*(t)$ and $c_{ij}^*(t)$ is:

$$c_{ij}^*(t) = f[v_{ij}(t), s_i^*(t - t_{ij})] \tag{2.7}$$

where $t_{ij}$ is the *transmission time* of the connection, and $v_{ij}$ is the *coupling coefficient* or *value* of the connection.

Taken together, the parameters $j_{ij}$, $v_{ij}$ form the *transmission function;* $v_{ij}$ may be constant or time-dependent. In the latter case it represents a *memory function* and can be made analogous to memory trace decay, discussed in Chapter 1. If the unit exhibits threshold properties similar to the expressions in (2.5) and (2.6), it is termed a simple A-unit. When $a_i^* = +1$, the unit is said to be *active.*

A *response unit* or *R-unit, $r_k$,* is a device which emits an output signal $r_k^*(t)$ in response to an input signal $c_{jk}^*(t)$. If

$$r_k^* = +1, \quad \text{when} \quad \Sigma c_{jk}^* > 0, \tag{2.8}$$

$$r_k^* = -1, \quad \text{when} \quad \Sigma c_{jk}^* < 0, \tag{2.9}$$

and

$$r_k^* = \pm 1, \quad \text{when} \quad \Sigma c_{jk}^* = 0, \tag{2.10}$$

i.e., the output is two-valued in the same manner as an adaline, then the R-unit is termed a *simple R-unit.*

Various interconnections of S-, A-, and R-units can be made to form several classes of perceptron. An example of a *simple perceptron* is shown in Fig. 2–18. It comprises S-units connected to A-units which in turn are connected to one R-unit. The values of the connections between the S- and A-units are all equal and fixed. The values of the connections between the A-units and the R-unit are variable and may be modified from time to time as part of the training process. The perceptron is *series-coupled,* that is to say that S-units connect only to A-units, which connect only to the R-unit (i.e., S → A → R). A simple perceptron degenerates into an *elementary perceptron* if the A- and R-units are *simple* units. With more than one R-unit, the network is referred to as a *series-coupled perceptron.*

If some connections join units of the same kind (i.e., S → S, A → A,

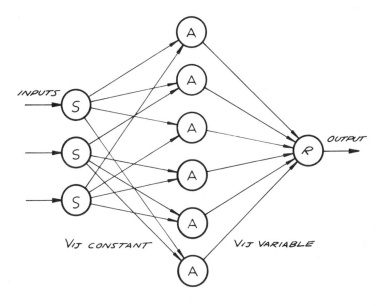

CONNECTIONS S→A→R

Figure 2-18 Simple perceptron.

R → R), the network is said to be cross-coupled and is called a *cross-coupled perceptron*. An example is shown in Fig. 2-19. Another style of connection is the *back-coupled perceptron* in which feedback occurs between levels (i.e., A → S, R → A). This is illustrated in Fig. 2-20. Yet other variations are possible if several layers of A-units are included. In this case the perceptron is said to be multilayered and begins to approach the concept of a cell mass.

Connections within the perceptron network are capable of modification or *reinforcement*. Several styles of reinforcement are possible. Thus, *positive reinforcement* is a process in which the value of the connection $c_{ij}$ is modified at a rate $dv_{ij}/dt$, which agrees in sign with the signal $u_j^*(t)$. In negative reinforcement $dv_{ij}/dt$ is opposite in sign from the signal $u_j^*(t)$. Another mode is *monopolar reinforcement*, in which the values of all connections terminating on an active unit remain the same unless $u_j^*(t)$ is positive. *Bipolar reinforcement* changes the values of connections regardless of whether the output of the terminal unit is positive or negative.

Instead of treating individual connections, all active connections can be reinforced uniformly, i.e., all connections $c_{ij}$ which terminate on some unit $u_j$ for which $u_j^*(t - t) \neq 0$ are changed to the same quantity. Connec-

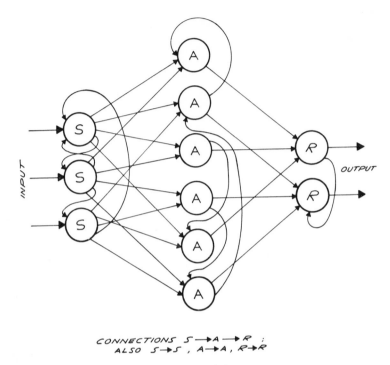

CONNECTIONS $S \longrightarrow A \longrightarrow R$ ;
ALSO $S \rightarrow S$ , $A \rightarrow A$ , $R \rightarrow R$

Figure 2-19 Cross-coupled perceptron.

tions which are inactive remain unchanged. Such reinforcement is called *α-system reinforcement* and a perceptron in which it is employed is called an *α-perceptron*. Another system has been designated γ-system reinforcement. Here the value of all connections to any unit are changed by a quantity

$$\Delta v_{ij}(t) = [w_{ij}(t) - (1/N_j) \sum_i w_{ij}(t)] \eta, \qquad (2.11)$$

where $w_{ij}(t) = 1$, when $u_i^*(t - \tau) \neq 0$,
$\qquad\qquad = 0$, when $u_j^*(t - \tau) = 0$,
$\quad N_j$ = number of connections terminating on $u_j$, and
$\quad \eta$ = reinforcement quantity.

Effectively, the value of the active connections is increased, the value of the inactive connections is decreased, and the total value of all connections remains the same. Thus the system may be described as conservative. An analogy may be seen between the fixed total value of the connections and the fixed total memory capacity of the brain.

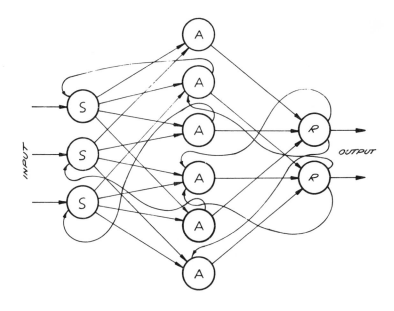

CONNECTIONS  S—→A —→R ; ALSO R—→A , A—→S

Figure 2–20 Back-coupled perceptron.

An experimental simple perceptron system contains the elements of Fig. 2–18, together with a reinforcement control system connected in the fashion of Fig. 2–21. The system is trained by changing the value of the connections between the association units and the response units according to one of the schemes discussed above, in response to information derived from specific signals.

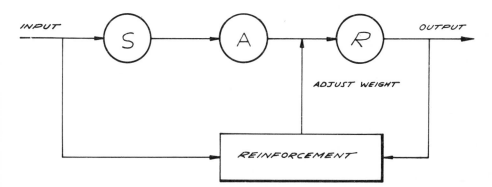

Figure 2–21 Simple perceptron system.

Thus, in *response-controlled reinforcement*, the value of the connections is changed by a constant amount whose sign depends on the current response. Another method, *stimulus-controlled reinforcement*, is a procedure in which the value of the connections is changed by a constant amount whose sign depends on the current stimulus. Yet another method, *error-corrective reinforcement*, is a procedure in which the values of the connections are changed when the current response is wrong. In this case the value is changed by an amount whose sign depends on the sign of the error.

To prevent a continual growth in the magnitude of the value of any connection, it is possible to constrain it to exhibit saturation, or to introduce some form of time-dependent decay. In this case the value of the connection depends not only on the training and reinforcement procedures but also on the frequency of occurrence of the stimuli. Once again, there is a strong resemblance to memory trace behavior.

The manner of interconnection of successive layers of units has also been formalized. Thus, a *binomial* model is one in which units in the second layer are connected to units chosen at random in the first layer. Each unit in the second layer has the same number of inputs. The connections may be excitatory or inhibitory. In a *Poisson* model with *constrained origins*, each unit in the first layer has the same number of outputs, which connect to units chosen at random in the second layer. In a *Poisson* model with *random origins*, the origin and terminal point for each connection are selected at random.

In order to determine some of the fundamental properties of perceptrons, an experiment was simulated in which 400 S-units were arranged in a 20 × 20 matrix to form a retina which was assumed to be excited by various combinations of horizontal and vertical stripes. The S-units were connected to a variable number of A-units and these in turn were connected to a single R-unit. The system is depicted in Fig. 2–22. With the constraint that all units be simple units, we have an elementary perceptron.

One of the experiments was concerned with the ability to distinguish between the 20 possible horizontal stripes and the 20 possible vertical stripes. Using $\alpha$-stimulus controlled reinforcement, it was found that a binomial network with 300 A-units was needed to insure that this task could be learned under sequential training. For a Poisson network with constrained origins, some 600 A-units were needed. Under random training, the 300–A-unit binomial network was able to learn the dichotomy with 95 percent probability in approximately 200 trials. Changing to error-controlled reinforcement, the task was learned to a 95-percent confidence level in approximately 70 trials for sequential training and approxi-

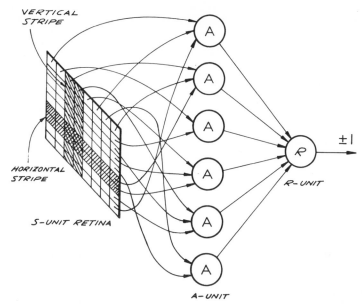

VERTICAL
STRIPE

A

A

A

±1

R

A

R-UNIT

HORIZONTAL
STRIPE

A

S-UNIT RETINA

A

A-UNIT

Figure 2-22 Perceptron discrimination experiment. For the sake of clarity, only a few connections are shown linking the S-unit to the A-unit. In fact, each retina cell is connected to at least one A-unit.

mately 80 trials for random training. An elementary $\gamma$-perceptron was able to perform these tasks in a similar fashion.

Three-layer series-coupled perceptrons possess a capability to perform any input-output association, i.e., connect any given input code with a given output code, provided only that the network can be made big enough. Success depends on the number of A-units available. The construction is by no means efficient, and the size of the network rapidly becomes uneconomical. Training may be accomplished by sequential presentation of successive stimuli (rote) or by random presentations. The learning time is usually shorter with rote training. The system is unable to generalize and is completely dependent on external evaluation during learning.

Cross-coupled and four-layer $(S \rightarrow A_1 \rightarrow A_2 \rightarrow R)$ perceptrons show an ability to generalize and have a shorter learning time than series-coupled perceptrons. In particular, systems with adaptive (modifiable) connections are able to learn groups of transformations from sequential stimuli. This effect occurs spontaneously without external interference. The cross-coupled system appears to be more dependent upon the sequence of input stimuli than the multilayer system, but both are much more susceptible to rote training than random training.

The back-coupled perceptron is the most difficult network to analyze; it also appears to have the most sophisticated response. Among other properties, it demonstrates *selective attention,* i.e., the ability to select familiar patterns masked by an unfamiliar background. The network may also be able to associate simultaneous but independent stimuli to improve its attention properties.

An important consideration in perceptron theory is whether, from a total stimulus world $W$, it is possible to make a given classification $C(W)$. In the case of a simple perceptron, this implies that all stimulus sets in $C(W)$ should be computed as $+1$, for instance, and all stimulus sets in $W$, but not in $C(W)$, should be computed as $-1$. To answer this question, let us consider two special constructions.

First, let the perceptron contain as many A-units as there are possible stimulus configurations, i.e., for $n$ two-valued inputs there will be $2^n$ A-units. Suppose that each A-unit is designated as associated with a particular stimulus configuration and that an excitatory connection is made between each S-unit which should be excited and the A-unit, and an inhibitory connection is made between each S-unit which should not be excited and the A-unit. Let the threshold of the A-unit be set to provide an output for the total excitation anticipated from the designated stimulus. Then one and only one A-unit will respond to any particular stimulus, and hence any dichotomy can be obtained by suitable adjustment of the A $\rightarrow$ R connection weight.

As the second construction, suppose the number of A-units is equal to the number of S-units, and one S-unit is connected to one A-unit. Then the system reduces to an adaline and the number of classifications which can be computed is limited by the number of linearly separable functions. Such a perceptron would be able to compute only a small fraction of the total possible stimulus sets and, therefore, could make an even smaller fraction of all possible classifications.

For practical configurations between these two extremes, it is possible to state only that, as the number of stimulus patterns contained in any $W$ *increases,* the probability that a randomly selected $C(W)$ can be computed *decreases.* If a computable $C(W)$ does exist, however, the perceptron can be organized in a finite time to perform such a function.[36]

The exact contribution to biology made by the study, analysis, and simulation of perceptrons is hard to assess. Certainly, perceptrons have shown that networks of threshold elements, connected in some involved and quasi-random manner, can learn to associate input-output codes, can generalize stimuli, and can select familiar stimuli from unknown ensembles. In $\gamma$-reinforcement, we may have a mechanism which is broadly analogous to memory trace. Furthermore, no matter which specific type of network we choose, learning is apparently easier with rote training than with random training. It remains to be seen if biologists and psychologists can establish more positive connections between the human brain and perceptron than are supplied by these tenuous threads.


## MEMBRANE MODELS

Neuron behavior is believed to depend on the ionic processes occurring in the *synapse-cell body-axon* complex. Painstaking examination of these areas has led to the development of a set of differential equations which describe pulse generation,[20] and these have been reduced to the familiar circuits of the analog computer.[23] By the use of electronic functions, the macroscopic behavior of sodium and potassium ion fluxes has been simulated, and models have been constructed which exhibit realistic pulse generation and other properties. Their exploitation, however, is more for the biologist attempting to study detailed intraneuron phenomena than the engineer interested in interneuron phenomena.


## NEURISTOR

The gross properties of the axon (as opposed to the membrane properties) have been used by H. D. Crane to develop a model which exhibits novel data processing properties. Called neuristor,[11,12,13] his model is a network in which signals are transmitted without attenuation in a manner similar to pulse propagation along an axon. This requires a distribution of energy sources along the signal channel so as to provide regeneration of the disturbance as each section of the network is triggered by its arrival.

The velocity of the propagating signal will depend on the elements of the networks. Once an individual section has been *discharged*, a certain time period will be required before it can be charged and ready for the succeeding pulse. This represents the *refractory* period. Since the portion of the network behind each disturbance is in a refractory state, two disturbances propagating towards each other in the same signal channel will annihilate one another when they *collide*.

The basic network comprises a chain of monostable devices, coupled so that each triggers the next. Such chains can be made so that the firing of any one device will produce a disturbance which propagates both up and down the line.

A neuristor can be implemented by interconnecting elements similar to that shown in Fig. 2-23. The resistance $R_1$ is so chosen that the quiescent

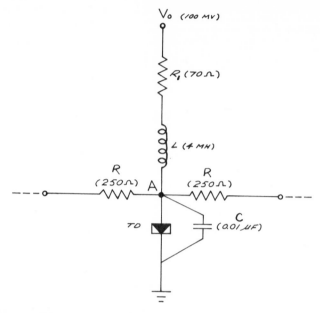

Figure 2–23 Monostable neuristor circuit element.

load line cuts the tunnel diode curve on the positive stable portion, close to the knee. When a signal appears at junction $A$, the tunnel diode is driven into its negative resistance region. The system is maintained in this state for some time by the energy stored in inductance $L$. When this energy has been released, the system returns to the quiescent operating point ready for another pulse.

A disturbance travels along the chain in a manner which depends on its original amplitude as shown in Fig. 2–24. If it is greater than a certain level (the asymptotic level), it gradually decays as it propagates until it attains that level; a disturbance which is less than the asymptotic level, but greater than the threshold level, gradually grows as it propagates until it attains that level; a disturbance which is less than the threshold level gradually decays to zero.[31]

Crane distinguishes two types of signal channels termed $F$ and $N$. The $F$ type is a *one-process* channel in which energy flow depends directly on the trigger wave. Its action is akin to a rechargeable chemical fuse (hence $F$ for fuse). The second is a *two-process* or $N$ type channel ($N$ for neuron) in which energy release may be initiated by an initial trigger wave and then modified or terminated by a second wave. Lines may also be designed with other characteristics; for instance, the release mechanism may depend on the time-derivative of the trigger pulse or on its amplitude.

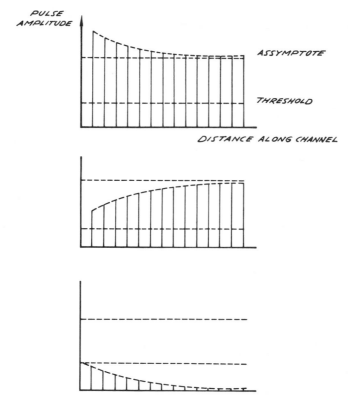

Figure 2–24 Behavior of tunnel diode model for different signal amplitudes.

When three or more neuristor lines join to form a connection, the result is known as T-junction (*T*rigger-junction). A signal impinging on the junction from any one line will excite all other lines, producing pulses which propagate away from the connection on all lines except that providing the stimulus. Reflection back along the stimulus line is not possible because of the refractory nature of the discharge. In another connection, lines may be coupled together so that they are mutually refractory (although one will not trigger the other). This is known as an R-junction (*R*efractory-junction). Symbolic diagrams for these connections are shown in Fig. 2–25.

Of particular significance is the T–R-junction which effectively performs an *exclusive-or* function. When a signal is applied at *A*, it propagates towards the junction, inhibiting any signal on *B*. On reaching the junction, a pulse is triggered on *C*. No pulse is transmitted back along *B* since the chain is in a refractory state. The occurrence of simultaneous

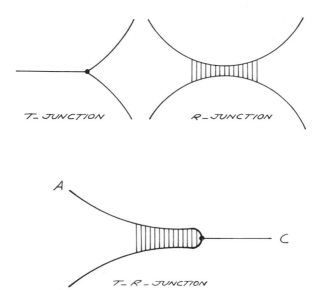

Figure 2–25 Neuristor connections.

pulses on *A* and *B* produces mutual refractoriness and annihilation of both signals.

Another connection, shown in Fig. 2–26, is unindirectional and frequency limited. Provided the mutual refraction is timed correctly, a pulse generated at *A* will never reach *B*. However, a pulse generated at *B* will always reach *A* provided sufficient time has elapsed since the last pulse to allow the refractory connection to be repaired. A structure analogous to a diode *or-gate* is readily formed with this connection.

Another computer-type device which can be made quite simply is a recirculating storage element or slow-speed clock. If a neuristor line is closed on itself so as to form a ring somewhat longer than that corresponding to a refractory period, and T-, R-, and T–R-junctions are intro-

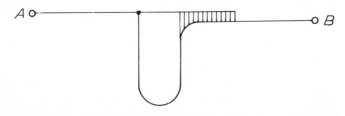

Figure 2–26 Unidirectional connection.

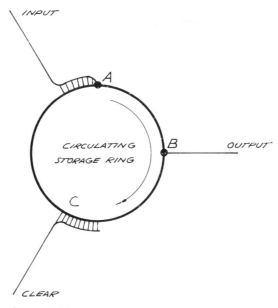

Figure 2-27 A storage ring using neuristor principles.

duced, as shown in Fig. 2-27, a pulse injected at *A* will produce a repetitive output at *B* until it is annihiliated by application of a pulse on the clear line.

Neuristor lines can also be interconnected without disturbance of the propagation paths of each line. Figure 2-28 shows the connections required. In effect, the R-junctions form guard connections which annihilate the unwanted signals spreading from the central T-junction.

There is no evidence to show that any of the connections described above appear in nature, although *inhibition* may bear some relation to the neuristor mechanism. In truth, what we have here is a construction which mimics pulse propagation along the axon, and which can be used to form computer-type elements in novel ways. Such novel approaches may one day lead to new component implementations.

## TRANSISTOR MODELS

As knowledge of electronic circuits has developed, and more versatile components have become available, various attempts have been made to simulate the detailed external behavior of a neuron by means of vacuum tube and transistor circuits. Early models[42] were almost entirely con-

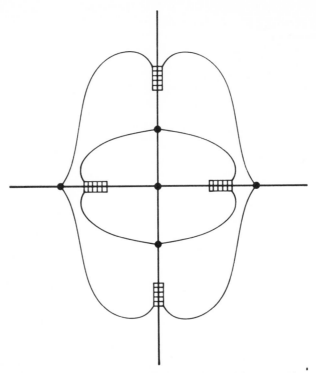

Figure 2-28 Interconnection of neuristor lines with preservation
of signal channel integrity.

cerned with the axon and copied the passive properties of the nerve fiber
as if it were a lossy transmission line. With the advent of digital techniques, a number of models have been designed which simulate neuron
performance in varying degrees.

A basic functional diagram is shown in Fig. 2-29. The input signals are
combined in a resistance network and applied to the trigger input of a
one-shot (OS #1). When sufficient input signals are present to force the
level above the triggering threshold, OS #1 fires and generates a relatively
long duration pulse which represents the refractory period of the neuron.
Until OS #1 resets, the circuit is made immune to further inputs. Firing
OS #1 triggers OS #2 which generates a short pulse representing the
neuron delay. The trailing edge of this pulse is differentiated to form a
narrow spike and is applied to a delay line which simulates axon propagation.

L. D. Harmon has designed a transistor circuit[16,17,39] which models *sum-
mation, threshold, excitation, inhibition, refractoriness,* and *delay* but not
*propagation.* The model consists of five transistors and has five *excitatory*
inputs and one *inhibitory* input. The output is an emitter follower which

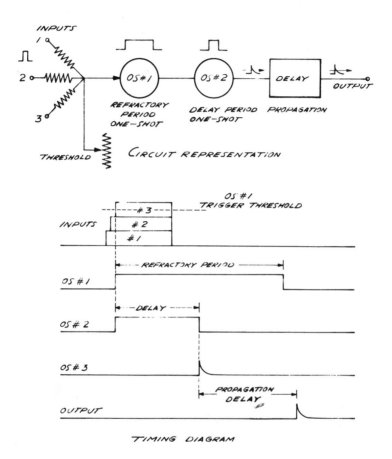

Figure 2-29 Electronic simulation of neuron.

provides sufficient power to drive the inputs of several other units. Other models have been reported by Johnston,[21] Mueller,[30] and McGrogan.[29]

Such circuits are useful in modeling small networks. By judicious modification of the input circuitry, it is possible to make models having a larger number of inputs. However, care must be taken to improve the stability of the threshold level, since, as the number of inputs increases, the allowable voltage variation between not-firing and firing decreases.

## MULTI-APERTURE MAGNETIC CORE NEURON

The multi-aperture magnetic core[1,10,34] has also been applied to the simulation of neuron behavior. Since it offers a relatively sophisticated model of the external properties without an unduly large number of components, its operation will be described in some detail. Specifically, A. E. Brain[6] has described a circuit which exhibits the properties of *multiple input, control of threshold level,* and a *variable amplitude output pulse.* The output weighting can be varied by signals from other parts of the system and provides a mechanism for *adapting* the input to succeeding stages.

The operation of the multi-aperture core shown in Fig. 2–30a depends on the flux distribution around four small holes. Their size is chosen so that the total magnetic cross section around the core periphery remains constant. Application of sufficient current in a winding such as *a* will saturate the magnetic material and the magnetic domains will be aligned in one direction as in Fig. 2–30b. If winding *b* is energized so as to oppose the major mmf (magnetomotive force) of *a*, it is possible to reverse the magnetization of some or all of the magnetic material outside of the dotted line in Fig. 2–30a.

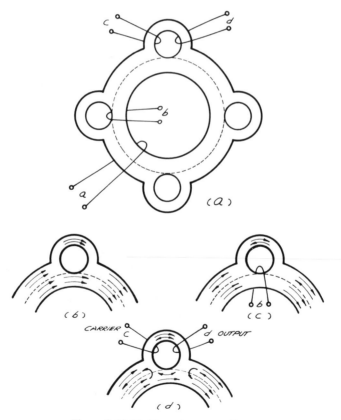

Figure 2–30 Multi-aperture magnetic core.

The flux distribution approximates that shown in Fig. 2–30c. The material within the inner half of the ring remains magnetized in the direction originally set by a, since this is the section of the core having least reluctance. For the same reason, it is the inner surface of the small hole which is demagnetized and remagnetized in the opposite direction. If a high-frequency carrier is now applied to winding c, as in Fig. 30d, the magnetization of the ring of magnetic material around the inside of the hole can be made to alternate and provide an output on winding d. The amplitude of this signal will depend on the steady demagnetization caused by b and the magnitude of the carrier current in c.

With these basic properties in mind, we can now proceed to discuss the operation of the circuit shown in Fig. 2–31. A blocking winding is wound around the center leg of one of the small holes of Core 1 and a

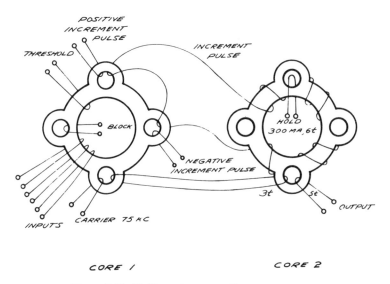

Figure 2–31 Multi-aperture magnetic core neuron.

hold winding is wound around a similar leg in Core 2. If all other windings are quiescent (i.e., not excited), they produce the flux patterns shown in Fig. 2–32a. Threshold is established by a winding around a main leg of Core 1 which may aid or oppose the blocking winding. The input windings may also aid or oppose the blocking winding.

Under appropriate conditions, the combined mmf's of these windings are sufficient to negate the blocking and the major loop of the core switches to establish the flux pattern of Fig. 2–32b. If pulses are then applied to the positive increment winding, they will be coupled to Core 2 and

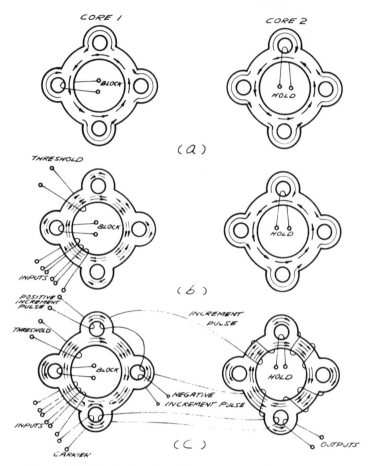

Figure 2–32 Functioning of a multi-aperture magnetic core neuron.

will eventually cause it to switch in a similar manner to establish the flux pattern shown in Fig. 2–32c. The carrier is now coupled through the appropriate small hole in Core 1, to the small hole of Core 2, and to the output winding. The amplitude of the output will depend on the balance between the mmf's of the hold winding and the increment winding, and can be varied (weighted) by application of positive or negative increment control pulses.

The advantage of this representation is that it requires only two magnetic elements per neuron; its disadvantages are that the winding of multi-aperture elements is quite difficult, and the hysteresis effects tend to make the detailed performance erratic. Furthermore, the reproducibility of the elements leaves something to be desired, although this is being improved with the development of new magnetic materials and manufacturing processes.

## BINARY LOGICAL ELEMENT

The *binary logical element* is a model which makes almost no pretense of duplicating neuron properties, but which, nevertheless, can be used to simulate simple learning phenomena.[8] A development of the *artron* (*artificial neuron*) of R. J. Lee,[14] it is a predominantly binary device. An $n$-input/1-output network is shown in Fig. 2–33. The inputs (1, 0) are applied to a minterm matrix which responds to any input function $f(x_1, x_2, \ldots x_n)$ by generating a signal on one of $2^n$ lines.

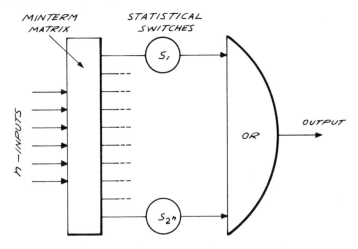

Figure 2-33 *n*-input/1-output binary logical element.

Each line is permanently associated with a specific minterm and with a *statistical switch.* Learning produces a variation in the probability of the switch being found open or closed. An *untrained* switch has an equal probability of being in either state. As learning progresses, the statistics are biased towards totally open or totally closed. The output (if any) from the switch passes to a $2^n$-input *or*-gate and to the output lead.

Since all possible combinations of the $n$-input terms are accommodated in the minterm matrix, and each minterm is associated uniquely with a two-position switch, it is apparent that all $2^{2^n}$ Boolean functions can be computed. Without formalizing the argument, it should also be apparent to the reader that the network responds without bias towards one function or another.

The manner in which statistical switch performance should change from random openings and closings to a completely open or completely closed state has been analyzed. If a signal sequence has $f$ signals that say the switch should be closed and $g$ signals that say the switch should be open when the reward and punishment signals are equally reliable, then

$$P(s) = \frac{1}{1 + \left(\dfrac{1 - z}{z}\right)^{f-g}}, \qquad (2.12)$$

where $P(s)$ is the probability of the switch being open (closed), and $z$ is the level of certainty of reward (punish) signals. Values of $P(s)$ are plotted against $(f - g)$ in Fig. 2–34 for various levels of confidence in the

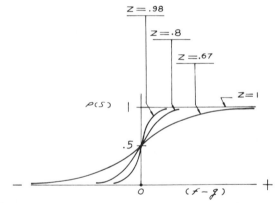

Figure 2–34 Theoretical learning curves for an ideal statistical switch.

goal circuit signals. They are the effective learning curves for an ideal switch. If the goal circuit is completely correct in its evaluation of the situation, i.e., $z = 1$, the statistics can be changed from 0.5 (untrained) to 0 or 1 (open or closed) with only one measurement of performance. Under these conditions, the network can be completely organized by $2^n$ measurements.

A block diagram of a statistical switch is shown in Fig. 2–35. The switching function is performed by the *and*-gate in the top right-hand corner; its state is determined by the *switch state flip-flop*. A logical 1 is equivalent to a closed switch and a logical 0 means an open switch.

The bias signal which determines the statistical function of the random function generator is controlled by the counter. A mid-count state of the

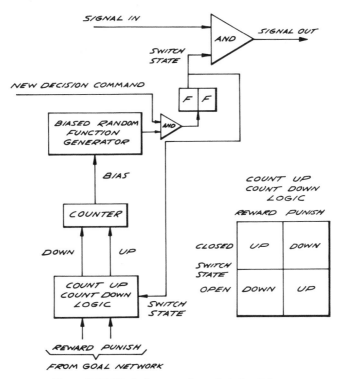

Figure 2-35 Block diagram of a statistical switch.

counter produces a bias such that the probability of obtaining a closed switch (open switch) at the next decision command is 0.5. A higher state in the counter will give an increased probability of obtaining a closed switch on the next trial, and a lower count state will decrease this probability.

The switch maintains a given open-closed decision (state of the flip-flop) until it is instructed to make a new decision (new decision command). This feature is included to assist the logic designer by simplifying the circuit timing. In normal operation, a *new decision command* would be generated just prior to entry of the input data. The counter state, and hence the probability that the switch will be open (closed), is adjusted by the application of reward and punish signals from the goal circuit in the manner shown in the table in Fig. 2-35.

Figure 2-36 shows a block diagram of the 2-input/1-output network. The input signals *a, b* are each applied to the trigger input of a one-shot. With no signal present, these circuits generate a level corresponding to *a* or *b*. When a signal occurs, they are triggered and generate a pulse corresponding to *a* or *b*. Four *and*-gates are connected in such a fashion

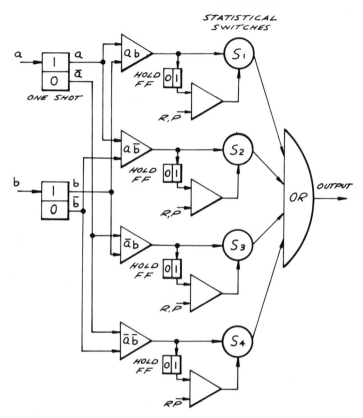

Figure 2-36 Two-input/one-output binary logical element.

that one, and only one, will respond to any possible input combinations, i.e., $a.b$; $\bar{a}.b$; $a.\bar{b}$; $\bar{a}.\bar{b}$. The signal is then passed to the statistical switch and to a hold flip-flop which stores the fact that that particular gate responded to the input signal combination. If the statistical switch is closed, the signal passes to the *or*-gate and appears as the output signal. If the statistical switch is open, the signal cannot pass, and there is no output signal. Thus, an output signal may or may not be generated in response to a specific input.

Depending on the nature of the signal, and on its evaluation of performance, the goal circuit will generate a reward or a punishment signal. This is applied, by means of the *and*-gate enabled by the *hold flip-flop*, to the proper statistical switch. Upon completion of the reward or punish operation, the hold flip-flops are cleared and the network is ready for the next signal.

The binary logic element can be expanded to provide a multiple output capability by adding statistical switches and *or*-gates as shown in Fig. 2-37. However, this construction requires a good deal of hardware. Since, for a specific input signal, only those switches which connect the unique minterm gate to the output *or*-gate(s) are contributing to the per-

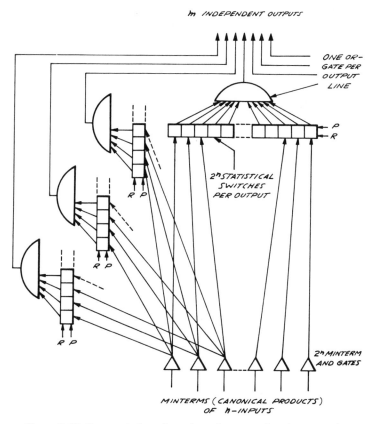

Figure 2-37 Representation of an *n*-input/*m*-output learning network.

formance of the network, a reduction in size and cost can be achieved by time-sharing circuits. If the state of each switch is stored in a central memory unit (core or drum) rather than in individual counter circuits, a further reduction in hardware can be achieved. The block diagram of a practical system is shown in Fig. 2-38.

The statistical state of the switches is stored as a binary number and is read out to the output generator on command. Selection of the storage

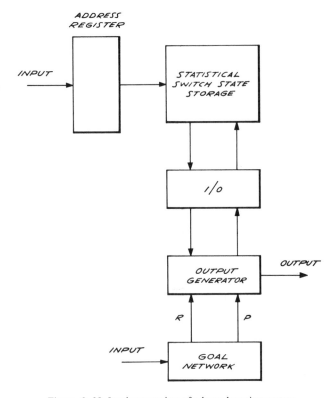

Figure 2–38 Implementation of a large learning system.

location for each switch can be directed by the minterm associated with it. The output generator comprises as many statistical switches as the number of required outputs. Upon generation of the output function, reward and punishment signals are applied to the statistical switches in the output generator and the updated statistical states are then returned to storage.[15]

If system time is available, a further reduction can be made by implementing only one statistical switch. This would be shared by the output generator stations. Finally, if the system is optimized so that the goal network can determine whether the action of the learning network is good or bad on the basis of one comparison, only one bit of information is required to show whether the switch should be open or closed and the system can be implemented by a smaller storage unit and a series of *and*-gates for the output generator. Such a system lends itself very readily to programming on a small general-purpose computer.

## CONDITIONAL PROBABILITY COMPUTER

Finally, let us consider the use of conditional probability in a machine which simulates reflex behavior. Called a *conditional probability computer,* this type of device has been pioneered by A. M. Uttley.[37,38] The principle is illustrated in Fig. 2–39. The three binary inputs *a, b,* and *c* are applied to three accumulators which count the number of pulses occurring on each line, divide by the total number of signal combinations presented, and store this number—the probability of occurrence of *a, b,* and *c* in any sequence of input words. The second tier accumulates the probability of occurrence of two simultaneous pulses, i.e., *a.b, a.c,* and

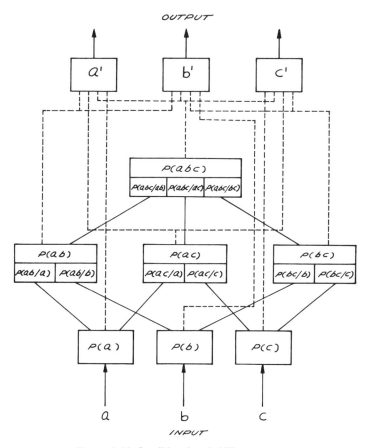

Figure 2–39 Conditional probability computer.

b.c, and the third tier computes the probability of occurrence of three simultaneous pulses, i.e., a.b.c.

After a suitable training cycle in which the various inputs have been applied to the machine (in sequence), the probability values will stabilize. The network can then be used to form outputs $a'$, $b'$, and $c'$ based on these values and the particular inputs present. Thus, if the training sequence has been such that $a.b$ always occurred, $P(ab) = 1$. If a fault now develops in $b$ so that its input is intermittent or completely absent, the $P(ab)$ accumulator will energize $a'.b'$ whenever $a$ occurs. In this way the computer can be used to restore faulty data to its most likely form.

As another example, suppose that inputs $a$ and $b$ represent a stimulus code, and $c$ represents the desired response, then the network might be trained as follows:

| | Stimulus | | Response |
|---|---|---|---|
| | $a$ | $b$ | $c$ |
| 1. | 0 | 1 | 0 |
| 2. | 1 | 0 | 1 |
| 3. | 1 | 1 | 1 |

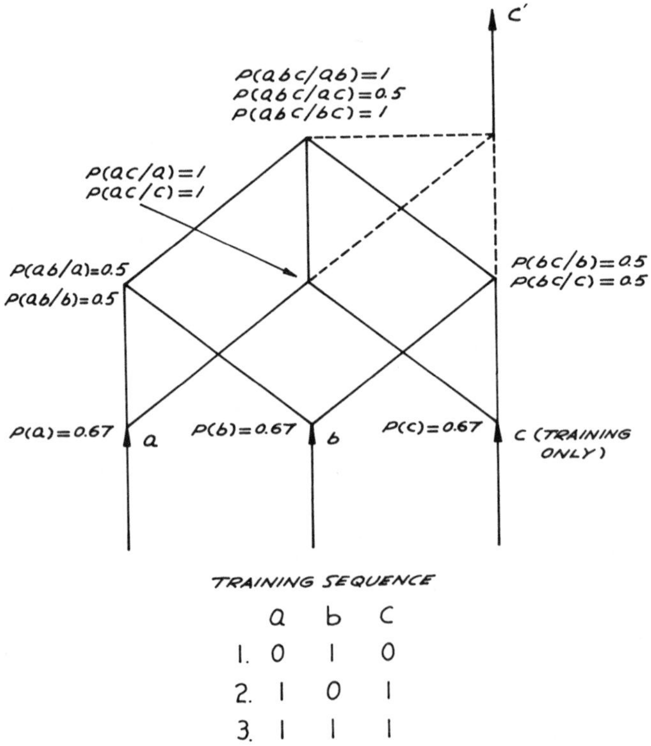

Figure 2-40 Example of conditional probability computer operation.

The application of these three patterns in sequence will form the probability values given in Fig. 2–40. After training, the input $c$ is removed, and the stimuli are applied at $a$ and $b$. Upon application of the first pattern stimulus (0, 1) we find $P(bc/b) = 0.5$, i.e., the network is noncommittal, and no output is generated at $c'$. In the case of the third stimulus (1, 1), $P(abc/ab) = 1$, and an output is generated at $c'$ again. The training sequences have thus been duplicated with the response $c'$ (which mimics $c$) being properly generated in response to the coded stimulus $ab$. In a biological environment this corresponds to reflex behavior.

A conditional probability computer requires $2^n$ elements (accumulators) to form an $n$-input/$n$-output network. It may be refined somewhat by the addition of an exponential decay to each of the probability elements so as to simulate time-dependent memory. Techniques have also been developed for temporal and spatial pattern processing.

## DISCUSSION

From the foregoing material it is apparent that the key to successful neuron modeling has yet to be discovered, and that a great deal has to be done before we know the nature of the locks which bar the way to the realization of a complete neuromime. Our presentation has ranged over the major approaches to neuron modeling and has included techniques which bear only a passing resemblance to a biological system. That this should be so is indeed fortunate, for a slavish imitation of the details of nature will not necessarily result in an electronic learning system. Proper use of some of the data which has been collected will undoubtedly result in major system breakthroughs; however, other techniques not related to current models should not be overlooked. We must seek to learn the biological principles involved and apply them within the context of the materials available. The thrill of flight eluded our forefathers, not because they could not copy nature in detail, but because they did not know how to make use of the principle of the generation of lift by an airfoil. The wheel is unknown in living systems; yet it represents an artificial device which allows us to amplify our natural capabilities immeasurably.

One of the locks which must be opened is associated with the problem of computability. On the one hand, we have devices which can form all possible Boolean functions, but whose complexity increases as $2^n$. Even with $10^{10}$ elements this means that one can, in general, have a network with only some 30 inputs. (The cerebral cortex is believed to be served by $10^8$ nerve fibers.) At the other extreme we have examples of threshold devices whose classifying ability is limited to the linearly separable functions, but whose effective capacity is increased somewhat by various degrees of generalization. In either case, for more than a few inputs, *uni-*

TABLE 2–1. Comparison of Major Properties of Neuron Models

| Model | Neuron Properties | | | | | Learning Properties | | Implementation | | | | | Comments |
|---|---|---|---|---|---|---|---|---|---|---|---|---|---|
| | Excitation | Inhibition | Refractoriness | Delay | Propagation | Adaptation | Generalization | Status | Type of logic | No. of inputs | No. of outputs | No. of computable functions* | |
| Formal neuron (W. S. McCulloch; W. A. Pitts) | Y | Y | Y | Y | N | N | N | t | T | n | 1 | LSF | Theoretical model; demonstrates stability of computation under changes of threshold and compensates for errors. |
| Automaton (J. von Neumann) | Y | Y | N | Y | N | N | N | t | T or M | n | m | $2^{2^n}$ | Theoretical model; provides building block for large networks which compute any function and correct errors. |
| Adaline/madaline (B. Widrow)· | Y | Y | N | N | N | Y | Y | h | T | n | m | $\approx 2^n$ | Threshold device, which adapts and can generalize, particularly in multilayers; computing capacity limited. |
| Perceptron (F. Rosenblatt) | Y | Y | N | N | N | Y | Y | h | T | n | m | LSF | Model includes sensors and response units; various intraconnections give ability to generalize. |

| Model | | | | | | | | | | | Remarks |
|---|---|---|---|---|---|---|---|---|---|---|---|
| Harmon neuron (L. D. Harmon) | Y | Y | Y | N | N | N | h | T | n | 1 | LSF | Transistor implementation; can be used to simulate biological networks; no. of inputs limited by threshold stability. |
| Multi-aperture magnetic core neuron (A. E. Brain) | Y | Y | Y | N | N | N | h | T | n | 1 | LSF | Transfluxor implementation; output signal level can be varied; fine properties of magnetic components not stable. |
| Neuristor (H. D. Crane) | — | — | — | Y | N | N | h | T | — | — | — | Models axon propagation; can be used to make novel computer-type elements. |
| Binary logic element (P. H. Halpern) | Y | N | N | N | Y | N | h | B | n | m | $2^{2^n}$ | Binary device which adapts; does not generalize. |
| Conditional probability comp. (A. W. Utley) | Y | N | N | N | ? | ? | h | B | n | n | $2^{2^n}$ | Probability model, which demonstrates reflex action; can predict parameter occurrence and correct errors. |

*For $n$-input/1-output device.
Abbreviations: Y = yes; N = no; ? = maybe; h = hardware; t = theoretical; T = threshold; M = majority; B = binary; LSF = logically separable functions.

*versality*, i.e., the ability to compute all possible functions connecting input and output, becomes quite impractical.

Much of this difficulty is related to the general assumption that, in our models, binary coding is adequate and reasonable. Certainly more efficient schemes using multivalued logic and time position coding can be devised. However, they add to the complexity of the hardware implementation and are not particularly attractive within the current state-of-the-art of electronic devices. Of course, one way of making better use of the capability which is available is to use *a priori* information so that only those connectives known to be needed to perform a specific function are included in the network. In effect this replaces a large *general-purpose* network, which can do anything, with a smaller *special-purpose* network which can only do some things.

As a case in point, consider the problem of selecting the correct postage stamp for a letter. In practice this is a matter of selecting a stamp or stamps from a roll (or a book) known to contain stamps of the appropriate denomination. It is not necessary to be able to identify the stamp correctly from all other stamps issued anywhere in the world, nor is it necessary to know all of the various combinations of weight, size, and cost which make up the postal rate table, although such knowledge could properly be required of a general-purpose stamp selection device. At the most, it is a matter of picking the correct roll or book of stamps from perhaps two or three and deciding whether to use one or two stamps according to one's estimate of the weight.

There is no evidence to show that the human nervous system is a universal network. For most situations, decisions are made on the basis of generalities and not on the fine structure of the data. If detail is required, it is usually only associated with a particular facet of the problem.

The major properties of the models discussed in this chapter are tabulated in Table 2–1. They are grouped in terms of: the basic neuron properties simulated; learning properties; and the nature of the implementation. For the reasons stated previously, the membrane models are ignored.

Of the neuron models which have been reduced to hardware, that which most nearly imitates the biological characteristics is the Harmon neuron. It lacks only propagation to be a full simulation. This is available in neuristor, and a combination of the two can provide all of the basic neuron properties for system simulation. The multi-aperture magnetic core can also be used in this fashion if delay is not important.

Learning, in the sense of adaptation and generalization, is manifest by adaline and perceptron. In the sense of a universal classifying system, it is demonstrated by a binary logical element, and in the sense of prediction and error correction, it is shown by a conditional probability computer.

As far as the theoretical models are concerned (i.e. formal neuron and automaton), the one inspired the other. Formal neuron is a logical model which expresses most of the basic neuron properties. It can be expanded into a device with any number of inputs, or groups of formal neurons may be interconnected. While this flexibility leads to all kinds of interesting results, it is hard on the analyst and the theoretician who would reduce everything to order. Nevertheless, formal neuron does represent most of the gross properties of a biological neuron in a reasonably acceptable manner. Automaton is an attempt to reduce neuron functioning to the orderly world of the mathematician; thus a small number of elements are devised from which all other networks may be constructed. There is no evidence to show that these elements have any physical existence. Perhaps the most significant contribution these models have made to the engineering world is the development of redundant structures which exhibit an ability to perform a given task with much greater reliability than a single unit (see Chapter 6).

Much more remains to be done before a satisfactory algorithm for constructing a learning system is available. The development of a suitable neuron model is part of this task.

## REFERENCES

1. D. R. Bennion, H. D. Crane, "Design and Analysis of MAD Transfer Circuitry," *Proceedings, Western Joint Computer Conference (AFIPS)*, 1959, pp. 21–36.
2. H. D. Block, "The Perceptron: A Model for Brain Functioning, I," *Reviews of Modern Physics,* vol. 34, 1962, pp. 123–135.
3. _____, B. W. Knight, and F. Rosenblatt, "Analysis of a Four-Layer Series-Coupled Perceptron, II," *ibid.,* pp. 135–142.
4. M. Blum, "Properties of a Neuron with Many Inputs," *Bionics Symposium,* WADD Technical Report 60-600, 1960, pp. 55–80.
5. _____, "Properties of a Neuron with Many Inputs," *Principles of Self-Organization,* H. von Foerster and G. W. Zopf, eds., Pergamon Press, New York, 1962, pp. 95–119.
6. A. E. Brain, "The Simulation of Neural Elements by Electrical Networks Based on Multi-Aperture Magnetic Cores," *Proceedings, IRE,* vol. 49, 1961, pp. 49–52.
7. S. H. Cameron, "An Estimate of the Complexity Requisite in a Universal Decision Network," *Bionics Symposium,* WADD Technical Report 60-600, 1960, pp. 197–212.
8. E. B. Carne, E. M. Connelly, P. H. Halpern, and B. A. Logan, "A Self-Organizing Binary Logical Element," *Biological Prototypes and*

*Synthetic Systems,* E. E. Bernard and M. R. Kare, eds., Plenum Press, New York, 1962, vol. 1, pp. 311–330.

9. A. J. Cote, "A Neuristor Prototype," *Proceedings, IRE,* vol. 49, 1961, pp. 1430–1431.

10. H. D. Crane, "A High-Speed Logic System Using Magnetic Elements and Wire Only," *Proceedings, IRE,* vol. 47, 1959, pp. 633–673.

11. ———, "The Neuristor," *Principles of Self-Organization,* H. von Foerster and G. W. Zopf, eds., Pergamon Press, New York, 1962, pp. 403–415.

12. ———, "Neuristor—A Novel Device and System Concept," *Proceedings, IRE,* vol. 50, 1962, pp. 2048–2060.

13. ———, "Possibilities for Signal Processing in Axon Signals," *Neural Theory and Modeling,* R. F. Reiss, ed., Stanford University Press, Stanford, Calif., 1964, pp. 138–153.

14. L. O. Gilstrap, R. J. Lee, and M. J. Pedelty, "Learning Automata and Artificial Intelligence," *Human Factors in Technology*, E. W. Bennett, J. Degan, and J. Spiegel, eds., McGraw-Hill, New York, 1962, pp. 463–481.

15. D. F. Guinn, "Large Artificial Nerve Net (LANNET)," *IEEE Transactions on Military Electronics,* vol. MIL-7, 1963, pp. 234–243.

16. L. D. Harmon, "Artificial Neurons," *Science,* vol. 129, 1959, pp. 962–963.

17. ———, "Neural Analogs," *Proceedings, Spring Joint Computer Conference (AFIPS),* 1962, pp. 153–158.

18. ———, "Problems in Neural Modeling," *Neural Theory and Modeling,* R. F. Reiss, ed., Stanford University Press, Stanford, Calif., 1964, pp. 9–30.

19. A. M. Hilton, *Logic, Computing Machines and Automation,* Spartan Books, Washington, D.C., 1963.

20. A. L. Hodgkin and A. F. Huxley, "A Quantitative Description of Membrane Current and Its Application to Conduction and Excitation in Nerve," *Journal of Physiology,* vol. 117, 1952, pp. 500–544.

21. E. B. Johnston, "Neuromime Modeling of Sensory Pathways," *Biological Prototypes and Synthetic Systems,* E. E. Bernard and M. R. Kare, eds., Plenum Press, New York, 1962, vol. 1, pp. 142–147.

22. P. M. Kelly, "Problems in Bio-Computer Design," *Bionics Symposium,* WADD Technical Report 60-600, 1960, pp. 215–237.

23. E. R. Lewis, "An Electronic Model of the Neuron Based on the Dynamics of Potassium and Sodium Ion Fluxes," *Neural Theory and Modeling,* R. F. Reiss, ed., Stanford University Press, Stanford, Calif., 1964, pp. 155–189.

24. R. L. Mattson, "A Self-Organizing Binary System," *Proceedings, Eastern Joint Computer Conference (AFIPS),* 1959, pp. 212–217.

25. W. S. McCulloch and W. A. Pitts, "Logical Calculus of the Ideas Immanent in Nervous Activity," *Bulletin of Mathematical Biophysics*, vol. 5, 1943, pp. 115–133.

26. W. S. McCulloch, "Agathe Tyche, of Nervous Nets—the Lucky Reckoners," *Mechanization of Thought Processes*, Her Majesty's Stationery Office, London, 1959, vol. 2, pp. 613–625.

27. ———, "Background," *Bionics Symposium*, WADD Technical Report 60-600, 1960, pp. 51–54.

28. ———, "Logisticon," *Aspects of the Theory of Artificial Intelligence*, C. A. Muses, ed., Plenum Press, New York, 1962, pp. 105–114.

29. E. McGrogan, "Improved Neuron Models," *Proceedings, National Electronics Conference (NECON)*, 1961, pp. 302–310.

30. P. Mueller, "On the Kinetics of Potential, Electromolance, and Chemical Change in the Excitable System of the Nerve," *Journal of General Physiology*, vol. 42, 1958, p. 193.

31. J. Nagumo, S. Arimoto, and S. Yoshizawa, "An Active Pulse Transmission Line Simulating Nerve Axon," *Proceedings, IRE*, vol. 50, 1962, pp. 2061–2070.

32. A. Novikoff, "On Convergence Proofs for Perceptrons," *Mathematical Theory of Automata* (Microwave Research Institute Symposia Series, vol. 12), J. Fox, ed., Polytechnic Press, Polytechnic Institute of Brooklyn, Brooklyn, N.Y., 1963, pp. 615–622.

33. S. Papert, "Redundancy and Linear Logical Nets," *Bionics Symposium*, WADD Technical Report 60-600, 1960, pp. 181–195.

34. J. A. Rajchman and A. W. Lo, "The Transfluxor," *Proceedings, IRE*, vol. 44, 1956, pp. 321–332.

35. F. Rosenblatt, *Principles of Neurodynamics*, Spartan Books, Washington, D.C., 1962.

36. *Ibid.*, pp. 109–127.

37. A. M. Uttley, "Conditional Probability Machines and Conditioned Reflexes," *Automata Studies*, C. E. Shannon and J. McCarthy, eds., Princeton University Press, Princeton, N.J., 1956, pp. 253–275.

38. ———, "Temporal and Spatial Patterns in a Conditional Probability Machine," *ibid*, pp. 277–285.

39. W. A. van Bergeijk and L. D. Harmon, "What Good are Artificial Neurons," *Bionics Symposium*, WADD Technical Report 60-600, 1960, pp. 395–406.

40. L. A. M. Verbeek, "Reliable Computation with Unreliable Circuitry," *Bionics Symposium*, WADD Technical Report 60-600, 1960, pp. 83–91.

41. ———, "On Error Minimizing Neuronal Nets," *Principles of Self-Organization*, H. von Foerster and G. W. Zopf, eds., Pergamon Press, New York, 1962, pp. 121–133.

42. U. von Ebbecke, "Modellversuche zur Erlauterung der Nerven-reizung," *Handbuch der Biologischen Arbeitsmethoden,* E. Abderhasden, ed., Urban und Schwarzkopf, Berlin, 1928, abt 5, t.6, pp. 679–718.

43. J. von Neumann, "Probabilistic Logics and the Synthesis of Reliable Organisms from Unreliable Components," *Automata Studies,* C. E. Shannon and J. McCarthy, eds., Princeton University Press, Princeton, N.J., 1956, pp. 43–98.

44. _____, "The General and Logical Theory of Automata," *Cerebral Mechanisms in Behavior,* John Wiley, New York, 1957.

45. B. Widrow, "Generalization and Information Storage in Networks of Adaline Neurons," *Self-Organizing Systems—1962,* M. C. Yovitts, G. T. Jacobs, and G. D. Goldstein, eds., Spartan Books, Washington, D.C., 1962, pp. 435–461.

46. M. Blum, N. M. Onesto, and L. A. M. Verbeek, "Tolerable Errors of Neurons for Infallible Nets," *Redundancy Techniques for Computing Systems,* R. H. Wilcox and W. C. Mann, eds., Spartan Books, Washington, D.C., 1962, pp. 66–69.

# Chapter 3

# SIMPLE LEARNING SYSTEM

As a practical matter, a *learning system* is a system which seeks to perform a specific task by adjusting its internal organization on the basis of information derived from trial solutions. Starting as a unit with a certain intrinsic capability, it may learn to perform a single task (or several tasks) in a specified environment, in which case it is a rather costly substitute for conventional logic or a servomechanism, or it may seek to perform a given function (or functions) in *any* environment. In this case it exhibits properties not heretofore normally associated with the characteristics of electronic devices. The system may be built of hardware which attempts to simulate detailed neuron mechanisms, or it may consist of statistical devices having nothing in common with an individual neuron, which behave in the gross manner of a neural network.

For convenience, a simple learning system can be described in terms of the four component networks shown in Fig. 3-1. The *sensors* observe the local environment and provide data to the *learning network* concerning changes and conditions in the environment. The learning network re-

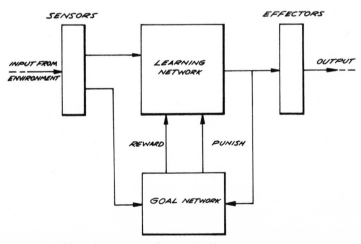

Figure 3-1. Block diagram of simple learning system

sponds to this input (*stimulus*) and develops an output (*response*) which actuates the *effectors*. Their action is evaluated by the *goal network,* which contains some statement of the system objective and a means of evaluating the system response on the basis of this objective.

In the untrained state (i.e., initially), the probability of the correct action being developed by the learning network is extremely small. However, progressive trial and error affords the opportunity for the goal circuit to influence the system and to change the state of the learning elements. If present performance is an improvement over immediately past performance, the goal circuit transmits a *reward* signal to the learning network to signify that an improvement has occurred. If present performance is worse than immediately past performance, a *punishment* signal is transmitted to the learning network to indicate that its performance has worsened. Reward reinforces the states of the network which contributed to the improvement and makes it more likely that they will occur again, while punishment tends to reverse the states of the elements which produced the improper output.

For any practical application: (1) the degree of organization of the learning network at a particular time should be proportional to the amount of information provided by the reward or punishment signals; (2) the goal network should provide a maximum amount of information to the learning network concerning the correctness or incorrectness of each specific action; (3) the design of the learning network should be such that a minimum amount of information is necessary to organize it to any particular state.

It is essential to an understanding of learning systems to realize that the learning network is organized to perform any function (within its intrinsic capacity) by external signals only, and that problem solving is a matter of determining the correct states for the learning elements by trial and error. The relative simplicity of this regimen implies that a longer time is needed to develop the solution to a problem than would be required by a device designed specifically for the particular application. In many situations a preliminary training period may be necessary. R. L. Beurle[1,2,3,4] has devised a more complex diagram than that in Fig. 3–1, which includes certain memory trace and association features. The central component is a mass of cells which are randomly interconnected, and whose performance is modified by the various signal inputs shown in Fig. 3–2, so as to favor particular activity. In the initial stages of learning (perhaps under the direction of a teacher), basic criteria are inserted in the *discriminator,* which provide very general guidance (sensations equivalent to *pleasure* and *pain*, for instance). The discriminator controls the response of the cell mass by reinforcing or inhibiting activity in accordance with its evaluation of the cell mass output for any particular situation. The development

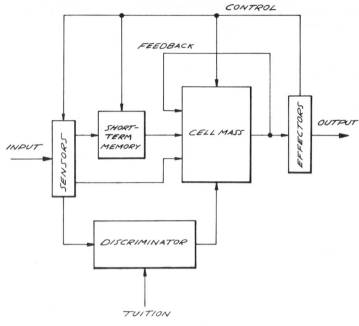

Figure 3–2. Representation of learning system

of certain connectives at the expense of the rest of the cell mass results in learning in the sense that these connectives are more likely to be formed in similar situations.

During the initial period of learning, when the discriminator has most to do (because few connectives have been established), the basic interconnection of the cell mass is established by the type of problem encountered. In this initial phase, short-term memory may be used to retain an individual stimulus until the discriminator is able to establish a satisfactory output (response). The *skeleton* so organized represents the implementation of the basic system goal since the fundamental organization of the cell-mass depends on the primary purpose specified for the system. Undoubtedly, in human and other living creatures, this is some form of the goal *survive.* Under normal circumstances, a machine will be organized to some secondary implementation of this goal so that the system will aid the broad spectrum of human endeavor directed towards human survival.

That one stimulus has succeeded in establishing a particular response implies that the organization of the cell mass should favor similar inputs. Thus, input association should be a relatively easy matter and should lead to generalization. Once the skeleton has formed, association between successive input stimuli can be forced by using the feedback loop to recirculate a previous event so that it is present when its successor arrives at the input to the cell mass. Alternatively, if the events are somewhat separated in time, the short-term storage can be used to retain one until the other occurs.

An extension of the system concept is shown in Fig. 3–3. It includes learning systems which perform the discriminator and subsystem control functions and provide additional computation capability. In principle, such a model can be expanded to include further layers of learning networks; however, this philosophical escalation adds little to the understanding of intelligence, or our capability at this time.

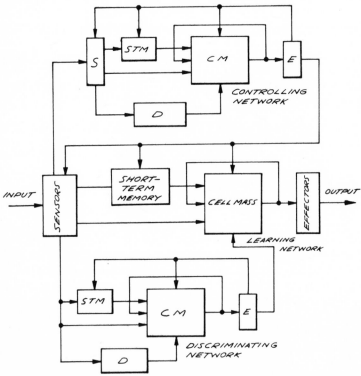

Figure 3–3. Learning system including adaptive discriminating and controlling networks. *CM* = Cell mass; *STM* = Short term memory; *S* = Sensors; E = Effectors; *D* = Discriminator.

## LEARNING NETWORK

Suppose there are a finite number of states which can be assumed by a learning network, and that there is a probability $p_k$ that the network will form connective $(k)$ under random training. Then the information required to organize the network to perform this may be defined as:

$$I_k = -\log_2 p_k \quad \text{(bits)} \tag{3.1}$$

This definition follows the classical work of Shannon[10] and has been used in connection with automata by von Neumann.[11] The average amount of information required to organize the network completely, i.e., all possible connectives, may be called the entropy, $H$, and is given by:

$$H = -\sum_k q_k \log_2 p_k, \tag{3.2}$$

where $q_k$ is the a priori probability that the system will be required to organize to connective $(k)$. For an optimum network, $p_k$ should be chosen to minimize $H$. This is equivalent to minimizing the expression

$$J = H + \lambda \sum_k p_k, \tag{3.3}$$

where $\lambda$ is the Lagrangian multiplier. Differentiating and equating to zero gives

$$\frac{dJ}{dp_k} = \frac{d}{dp_k}\left[-\sum_k q_k \log_2 p_k + \lambda \sum_k p_k\right] = 0. \tag{3.4}$$

Now,

$$\sum p_k = \sum q_k = 1 \tag{3.5}$$

Under these conditions, (3.4) reduces to

$$p_k = q_k, \tag{3.6}$$

i.e., to minimize the average amount of information required to organize the network completely, the probability of the network being predisposed to form connective $(k)$ should be equal to the probability that the network will be required to form this connective.[5] In effect this argument affirms that a special purpose device will perform the function for which it was designed more efficiently than a general purpose device. For a network which can form $m$ connectives, all of which are equally likely,

$$H_{\min} = \log_2 m, \tag{3.7}$$

and for a network which can form any Boolean function of $n$ variables,

$$H_{\min} = 2^n, \tag{3.8}$$

since $m = 2^{2^n}$.

As we have seen, many of the learning devices discussed utilize threshold logic and some are interconnected in a devious fashion making it well-nigh impossible to compute the total number of connectives which can be formed. Such systems may also be predisposed to form certain connectives more often than others due to bias in their internal structure. For networks composed of these elements, the foregoing result is only of academic interest. However, it may be applied to devices, such as the binary logical element, which fulfill the conditions used to derive (3.8).

For instance, it is possible to determine the average number of trials which must be made in order to organize a network of elements when the correctness of any response cannot be determined until several trials later. (This is typical of a maze problem in which the value of any given step must be assessed on the basis of whether it must be retraced at some later time, or whether it leads *home*.) If the amount of information obtained by observing that a sequence of $k$ trials is correct is $-\log_2 p_k$, where $p_k$ is the a priori probability that the sequence was correct, then the amount of information obtained by observing that the $k$ sequence is incorrect is $-\log_2 (1 - p_k)$.

Now, the fraction of the total functions which contain a certain $k$ inputs is $2^{-k}$, so that, if all functions are equally likely,

$$p_k = 2^{-k}. \tag{3.9}$$

The average amount of information (entropy) obtained by the observation of each $k$ sequence will be weighted by the probability of the outcome of the observation, i.e.,

$$H_k = -p_k \log_2 p_k - (1 - p_k) \log_2 (1 - p_k) \tag{3.10}$$

If $k$ is large, this reduces to

$$H_k = \frac{k}{2^k}. \tag{3.11}$$

Now, for an $n$-input/1-output classifying network, $2^n$ bits of information are required to organize it; hence, the average number of comparisons required will be

$$N = \frac{2^n}{H_k} = \frac{2^{n+k}}{k}. \tag{3.12}$$

As might be expected, the longer one must wait before being able to assess the truth of one event, the harder it is to organize the network; if the wait is too long, it will become almost impossible.

Table 3–1 shows some representative values of the number of comparisons required to organize a 1-output/multiple-input, binary logic element for various sequence lengths. The values for $k = 0$ represent the number of comparisons which, normally, will be required to organize the element if we have complete confidence in the information provided by the comparison.

TABLE 3-1. Number of Comparisons Required to Organize an
n-Input/1-Output Binary Logic Element

| Length of Sequence | $n = 2$ | $n = 3$ | $n = 4$ | $n = 5$ | $n = 6$ | $n = 7$ |
|---|---|---|---|---|---|---|
| $k = 0$ | 4 | 8 | 16 | 32 | 64 | 128 |
| $k = 5$ | 26 | 52 | 103 | 205 | 410 | 820 |
| $k = 10$ | 420 | 820 | $1.64 \times 10^3$ | $3.28 \times 10^3$ | $6.55 \times 10^3$ | $1.31 \times 10^4$ |
| $k = 20$ | $2.10 \times 10^5$ | $4.20 \times 10^5$ | $8.39 \times 10^5$ | $1.67 \times 10^6$ | $3.36 \times 10^6$ | $6.71 \times 10^6$ |

Let us now turn to the consideration of the second major network in a learning system, the goal network.

## GOAL NETWORK

The statement of fundamental objective provided to a learning system is known as the *goal*. Usually it is a simple command, such as: *keep moving, stabilize, translate, survive.* However, in any practical situation, such general directives must be reduced to sets of secondary commands which interpret the basic instruction in terms of the immediate environment. Thus the goal *survive* is manifest in living organisms in such terms as *stay away from excessive heat, take nourishment,* and, in our own case, *earn a living.*

Obviously there are a great many such secondary or sub-goals associated with everyday life. If man's primary goal is to survive, we may postulate a set of secondary, tertiary, ... *n*-ary goals, which fill in the fabric of civilization. Thus, the secondary goals may be to avoid obvious dangers, such as fire, and the tertiary goals might be associated with the search for food. In fact, the process of civilization may be the development of more and more specialized and detailed goal levels. While we cannot expect to endow machines with these attributes, it is nevertheless important that we realize that a typical characteristic of a learning system is its ability to develop sub-goals which implement facets of the primary goal.

To illustrate the detailed functioning of the goal network, consider the 2-input/1-output *binary logical element* shown in Fig. 3-4. A competitive coin-matching game was simulated with a human opponent attempting to call heads or tails, so that the binary logic element would not match it. If the element matched its opponent's call it was rewarded; and if it failed

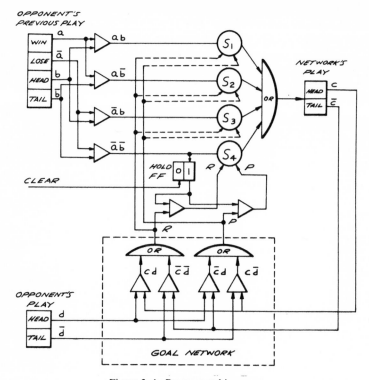

Figure 3–4. Penny-matching game

to match the call, it was punished.[6,7] Thus it became an aggressive player trying to match the opponent's moves as often as possible.[12] In deciding to reward or punish the network, the following payoff table was used:

|  |  | Operator | |
|---|---|---|---|
|  |  | *Heads* | *Tails* |
| **Binary Logic Element** | *Heads* | Reward | Punish |
|  | *Tails* | Punish | Reward |

A typical game-sequence is shown in Table 3–2 with a bias towards number of wins by the network. On examining the states (0–15) of the statistical switch counters it was found that channel $\overline{A}B$ indicated a count of 3 instead of the count of 7, which would be expected for random operation. This corresponded to the opponent's play of *tails and winning*.

TABLE 3–2. Competitive Penny-Matching Game Sequence

| Call — Heads or Tails | | Network Win — Lose | Number of Wins | |
|---|---|---|---|---|
| Opponent | Network | | Network | Opponent |
| H | H | W | 1 | |
| H | H | W | 2 | |
| T | T | W | 3 | |
| H | H | W | 4 | |
| H | H | W | 5 | |
| T | T | W | 6 | |
| T | T | W | 7 | |
| T | T | W | 8 | |
| H | H | W | 9 | |
| T | H | L | | 1 |
| T | H | L | | 2 |
| H | T | L | | 3 |
| T | T | W | 10 | |
| T | H | L | | 4 |
| T | T | W | 11 | |
| H | H | W | 12 | |
| H | T | L | | 5 |
| T | T | W | 13 | |
| H | T | L | | 6 |
| H | T | L | | 7 |
| T | T | W | 14 | |
| T | H | L | | 8 |
| H | T | L | | 9 |
| T | T | W | 15 | |
| T | H | L | | 10 |
| H | H | W | 16 | |
| T | H | L | | 11 |
| H | T | L | | 12 |
| H | T | L | | 13 |
| T | T | W | 17 | |
| T | T | W | 18 | |
| T | H | L | | 14 |
| H | H | W | 19 | |
| T | T | W | 20 | |
| H | T | L | | 15 |
| H | H | W | 21 | |
| H | H | W | 22 | |
| T | T | W | 23 | |
| H | T | L | | 16 |
| T | T | W | 24 | |
| H | H | W | 25 | |
| H | T | L | | 17 |
| H | T | L | | 18 |
| T | H | L | | 19 |
| H | H | W | 26 | |

Examination of the play showed that, more often than not, after a play of tails and winning, the opponent's next call was heads. The bias was detected by the network and used to advantage.

The problem for the network is, given the play of the opponent and whether he won or lost (i.e., whether the network mis-matched or matched), to predict the opponent's next call correctly. The opponent's previous play is coded so that $a$ denotes whether he won or lost, and $b$ whether he played a head or a tail. Thus:

$$ab = \text{opponent played head and won}$$
$$a\bar{b} = \text{opponent played tail and won}$$
$$\bar{a}b = \text{opponent played head and lost}$$
$$\overline{ab} = \text{opponent played tail and lost}$$

The output of the learning network represents the network's current play. It is coded:

$$c = \text{network plays head}$$
$$\bar{c} = \text{network plays tail}$$

and is applied to the goal network. The opponent's current play is also applied to the goal network and is coded:

$$d = \text{opponent plays head}$$
$$\bar{d} = \text{opponent plays tail}$$

The system goal (i.e., to match the play of the human opponent) is implemented by the combination of *and*-gates and *or*-gates shown in Fig. 3–4. The learning network is rewarded whenever a match occurs, i.e.,

$$R = cd + \bar{c}\bar{d}, \tag{3.13}$$

and is punished whenever a mis-match occurs, i.e.,

$$P = \bar{c}d + c\bar{d}. \tag{3.14}$$

The fact that the goal network is composed of logic elements implies that, although it is the only goal network for the system, it may not be the primary goal for the operation of matching. It is really an extension of the designer whose sub-goal was to build a learning system which would match plays against a human opponent. Therefore, although we may refer to the primary goal of a learning system, we should remember that a man's intelligence stands behind each design. A device built with human hands is normally intended to fulfill a purpose, and this will be reflected in its internal structure. Only man possesses a will which motivates his intellectual activity; an *intelligent machine* requires a set of criteria before it can fulfill the purpose for which it was designed.

Examination of (3.13) and (3.14) shows that they are a special case of the response of a 2-input/1-output binary logical network, and immediately suggests a way in which the goal network criteria can be developed, rather than being specified by the designer (although this does not alter the dependence on the designer). Consider the system shown in Fig. 3–5. It consists of two 2-input/1-output learning networks. One is the major network corresponding to the learning network of Fig. 3–4. The other is a subsidiary learning network which will eventually become the goal network.

The designer becomes a *teacher*, represented by the box in the center of the diagram. He is able to evaluate the performance of the learning network in attempting to match the opponent's play and can reward or punish the network accordingly. The output of the subsidiary learning

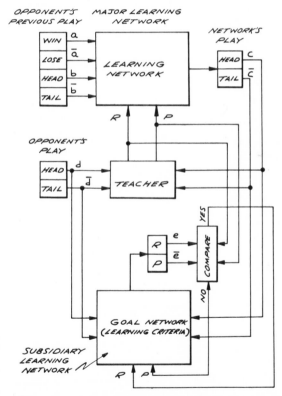

Figure 3–5. Development of goal criteria for penny-matching game using second learning network and human teacher in parallel

network (goal network) is coded as

$$R = e \qquad P = \bar{e} \qquad\qquad (3.15)$$

and is compared with the reward or punish signals applied by the teacher to the major learning network. After each play, if comparison exists, the subsidiary network is rewarded; if comparison does not exist, the subsidiary network is punished. Thus the subsidiary learning network is trained to mimic the teacher, and, after a sufficient number of trials, the teacher can withdraw, leaving a goal network containing the criteria necessary to direct the learning network in its game of penny-matching.

For convenience, these criteria are sometimes referred to as *learned goal criteria,* or more simply *learned criteria.* At any time, upon intervention of the teacher, the system can be reorganized about other goal criteria to perform another task, provided it is within the intrinsic capability of both networks. In this way, the designer does *not* have to work out the detailed design of the criteria circuits in the goal network; he has only to

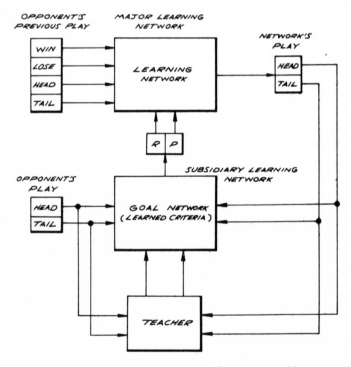

Figure 3–6.  Development of goal criteria for penny-matching game
using second learning network and human teacher in series

be able to evaluate the performance of the major learning network and to apply reward or punishment as required.[8]

Instead of training the goal network in parallel with the learning network, it is possible to achieve the same result with the networks in series as shown in Fig. 3–6. Here the teacher rewards or punishes the goal network on the basis of whether it provides the correct reward or punishment signal to the major learning network. This connection will require a greater number of trials than for the parallel training technique, before the total system is organized, since, as it learns, the goal network will provide a certain amount of erroneous data to the learning network. An extension of this principle allows us to construct tiers of learned criteria[9] as shown in Fig. 3–7.

In our present example of penny-matching, the advantage of using learned criteria instead of a unique combination of logic circuits may not be too apparent. For more complex tasks, however, they have a very real advantage since they can be organized by an astute observer rather than being completely and explicitly designed. In many situations, it is quite likely that it may be impossible to predict all of the unique criteria required. However, using a learning network to fulfill the goal network function, it is only necessary to ensure that it have sufficient input con-

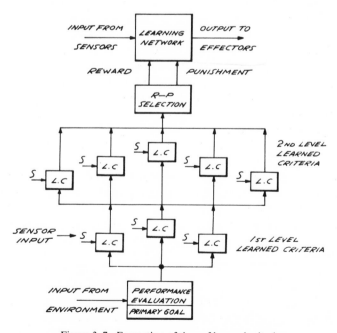

Figure 3–7. Formation of tiers of learned criteria

nections to accommodate the maximum number of system sensors, and to have a single output which can be interpreted in terms of reward and punishment.

## REINFORCEMENT

So far there has been a tacit assumption that the values of the reward and punishment signals are equal in value, i.e., for equal information they change the abscissa of the operating point on the statistical switch curve of Fig. 2–34 by an equal amount. There are many practical reasons associated with the logic design of a network which make this desirable. Nevertheless, certain special effects are worth mentioning:

1. If $R = 0$, $P = 1$, the network will organize to the complement of the desired function.
2. If $R = 1$, $P = 0$, the network will organize towards the desired function.

In both of these cases the time required will generally be much longer than for $R = P = 1$, since the goal network can affect only the organization for incorrect outputs or correct outputs.

Since a network can form many more incorrect answers than correct ones when it is required to match a particular stimulus to a given response, a correct output should receive a larger increment of positive reinforcement (reward) than the increment of negative reinforcement (punishment) which is given for an incorrect output. Such a scheme has been used in pseudo-random digital networks[6] formed by interconnecting 2-input/1-output binary logic elements.

Learning curves for a 5-input/4-output network are shown in Fig. 3–8. The probability of such a device generating the correct answer without training, if all answers are equally likely, is 6.25 percent. A bias in favor of the reward increment improves the learning time markedly, particularly as the 100-percent point is approached. However, a balance must be maintained. If the reinforcing increment is too large, the network states will be perturbed too violently, and the network will not stabilize. This effect is shown in Fig. 3–9 for a 2-input/3-output pseudo-random digital network. In this case the initial probability of forming the correct output is 12.5 percent.

As another logical deduction, it seems reasonable that learning should be aided by applying reinforcement to only those connectives which assisted in forming the output (correct or incorrect). If other elements are included, there is a distinct probability that the reinforcement will destroy connectives contributing to other stimulus-response associations.

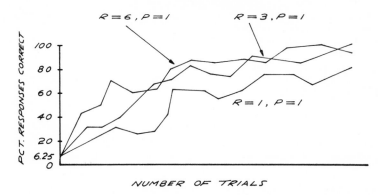

Figure 3–8. The effect of training a 5-input/4-output pseudo-random connected learning network with various values of reward (*R*) and punishment (*P*).

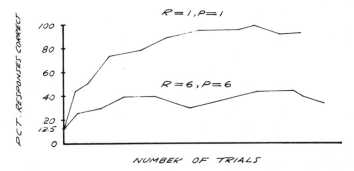

Figure 3–9. The effect of training a 2-input/3-output pseudo-random
connected learning network with too high a value of reward (*R*) and
punishment (*P*)

Consider a 3-input/2-output network formed from 2-input/1-output
binary logical elements (BLE) as in Fig. 3–10. The network was taught
the responses shown in the training table. Under *nonselective* reinforcement rules, the elements were all rewarded if the correct stimulus-response
association was formed. If it was not, all elements were punished. Under
partially selective reinforcement, the network was regarded as being composed of two equal parts, each contributing to an output. The halves were
rewarded or punished depending on whether their particular partial output was correct or incorrect.

Learning curves for these two modes of operation are shown in Fig.
3–11. They are compared to the performance of a 3-input/2-output
binary logical element, since this is a network in which reinforcement

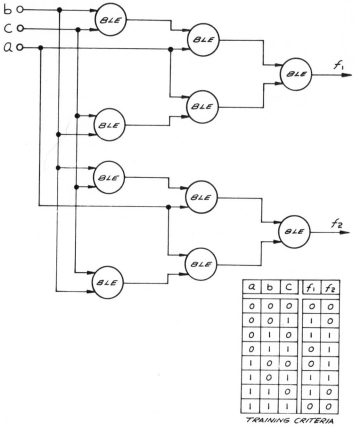

Figure 3–10.   Three-input/2-output network made from 2-input/1-output
binary logical elements

is uniquely selective.  It will be seen that localized application of correct
reinforcement improves the learning times substantially.

## ROTE LEARNING

Humans, and certain of the neuron models described in Chapter 2, appear to learn better if the data is presented in an orderly sequence.  This is
also true of pseudo-random digital networks.  Figure 3–12 shows learning
curves for a 5-input/4-output network trained by the repetitious pres-

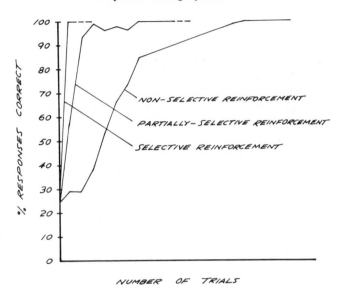

Figure 3-11.  Relationship of learning to type of reinforcement for
3-input/2-output digital network

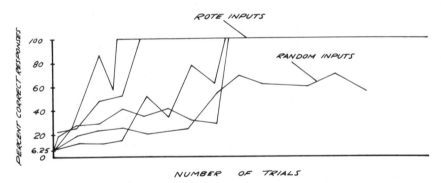

Figure 3-12.  Learning curves for 5-input/4-output pseudo-random connected learning
network trained with rote inputs and random inputs

entation of stimuli in sequence (by rote) and by the presentation of
the same stimuli at random.  The steep, final approach to complete
learning in the case of rote inputs is typical and appears to indicate
that after several successive presentations, in which conditions are laid
conducive to the basic order necessary to learn the particular tasks, the
complete organization of the network is established rapidly.

## DISCUSSION

In this chapter the elementary principles of learning system construction and function have been developed. This has been done by using specific examples of hardware which are easy to describe and whose operation is readily apparent. The binary logical element is a simple *classifying device,* i.e., an element in which a specific output can be associated with every possible input so that all combinations can be identified. However, the principles involved are applicable to any neuromime with only minimum changes to accommodate specific detail, and are generally applicable to learning networks independent of the implementation chosen.

A learning system has been characterized as comprising four major subsystems, two of which, the learning network and the goal network, may contain learning elements. Both networks can be organized in series by external instructions to perform a given mission. It is a simple extrapolation to consider all the learning elements to be contained in a single network with somewhat complex intranetwork connections so that the goal network degenerates to a single goal criterion. In similar fashion, certain functions of the sensor network can be integrated into the learning network, leaving a relatively elementary set of sensors.

Thus the arbitrary interposition of functional networks is not inconsistent with the known physical fact that the nervous system appears to be a mass of cells receiving inputs from sensors and providing instructions to effectors. If the goal criterion is provided by an external teacher until secondary goal criteria are learned, the whole subsequent learning process can occur within a network of learning elements.

## REFERENCES

1. R. L. Beurle, "Properties of a Mass of Cells Capable of Regenerating Pulses," *Philosophical Transactions of Royal Society of London,* series B, vol. 240, 1956, p. 55.
2. _____, "Storage and Manipulation of Information in the Brain," *Journal, Institution of Electrical Engineers,* vol. 5, 1959, pp. 75–82.
3. _____, "Storage and Manipulation of Information in Random Networks," *Aspects of the Theory of Artificial Intelligence,* C. A. Muses, ed., Plenum Press, New York, 1962, pp. 19–42.
4. _____, "Functional Organization in Random Networks," *Principles of Self-Organization,* H. von Foerster and G. W. Zopf, eds., Pergamon Press, New York, 1962, pp. 291–311.
5. E. B. Carne, E. M. Connelly, P. H. Halpern, and B. A. Logan, "A Self-Organizing Binary Logical Element," *Biological Prototypes and*

*Synthetic Systems,* E. E. Bernard and M. R. Kare, eds., Plenum Press, New York, 1962, vol. 1, pp. 311–330.

6. E. B. Carne, "A Study of Generalized Machine Learning," Aeronautical Systems Division, Technical Documentary Report ASD-TDR-62-166 (Contract AF33 (616)-7682), 1962.

7. _____, "Self-Organizing Models—Theory and Techniques," *Proceedings, National Aerospace Electronics Conference (NAECON),* 1962, pp. 499–508.

8. _____, "Representation of Complex Electronic Learning Systems," *IRE International Convention Record, 1962,* Part 9, pp. 64–67.

9. M. D. Mesarovic, "On Self-Organizational Systems," *Self-Organizing Systems—1962,* M. C. Yovitts, G. T. Jacobi, and G. D. Goldstein, eds., Spartan Books, Washington, D.C., 1962, pp. 9–36.

10. C. E. Shannon, "A Mathematical Theory of Communication," *Bell System Technical Journal,* vol. 27, 1948, pp. 379–423.

11. J. von Neumann, "Probabilistic Logics and the Synthesis of Reliable Organisms from Unreliable Components," *Automata Studies,* C. E. Shannon and J. McCarthy, eds., Princeton University Press, Princeton, N.J., 1956, pp. 43–98.

12. J. D. Williams, *The Compleat Strategyst,* McGraw-Hill, New York, 1954.

# PART II.
## APPLICATIONS

# Chapter 4

# PATTERN RECOGNITION

As discussed in Chapter 1, one of the capabilities which might be included in future generations of computers is the ability to examine, select, and group data from photographs, maps, charts, or books in such a way that they are ready for immediate entry into the machine without need of analyst intervention. This requires the ability to *recognize* patterns, i.e., to extract and identify the familiar from an environment containing this and other information.

Throughout life we constantly use such a talent as we wrestle with sensory patterns of one kind or another, recognizing situations, and providing responses on the basis of experience. Unfortunately, there is a tendency to associate pattern recognition exclusively with the faculty of sight. While visual images form the greater part of our input from nature, they are by no means the only stimulus, and all five senses contribute to the nervous patterns impinging on the brain.

Our knowledge of the environment very often depends on the interaction of data derived simultaneously from a combination of signals describing sights, sounds, smells, flavors, and textures. In some cases, although the basic stimulus is derived from a single sense, it evokes other stimuli or may be enhanced by later stimuli which are received by another sense. For instance, syllables and words are better recognized if *sounded-out,* and sentences may be better understood if *read aloud.* Poor spelling or imperfect writing is very often compensated by a knowledge of the context. Appreciation of a play is enhanced by seeing it performed, and the understanding of technical prose is often greatly improved by the critical observation of a well-chosen experiment.

The process of recognition may escalate to more abstract concepts. Thus, reading is first a matter of recognizing letters, then building syllables and words, and then making phrases and sentences. But it is also much more, for with practice it becomes a medium for the reception of thoughts and eventually for the development of intangible criteria for aesthetic enjoyment.

Of course, the reproduction of the more abstruse forms of pattern recognition is not to be expected from a machine. Indeed, one may ponder whether such forms are not peculiarly associated with human faculties. While a machine can reasonably be expected to detect symmetry and curvature, it is unlikely that it would advance to an appreciation of *beauty,* or that, if it did, such a function would contribute in any way to its usefulness. Similarly, *loyalty* is an attribute which develops out of the higher-order mental processes in man, but which would be of little importance to a machine. At the lower levels, however, where the universe admits a mechanistic approach, machines may one day be able to sort and classify data in a very commendable manner.

Whether the problem is concerned with visual images, with other single sensory inputs, or with a combination of sensory inputs, the signals presented to the brain consist of an astronomic number of neural impulses which have to be correlated. The only general purpose pattern recognizer extant appears to be man himself, who uses sensors of great complexity and amazing power. Attempts have been made to model some of the basic properties of the eye and the ear.

## CHRYSLER OPTICAL PROCESSING SCANNER

One aspect of the gross behavior of the eye which has been used in a character recognition system has been described by Buell[5] of Chrysler Corporation. In this system, an oscillating optical scanner is used to produce relative motion between the image and retina in imitation of the effect of the involuntary motions of the eyeball which appear in normal vision (see Chapter 1).

The character or shape to be recognized is projected onto a retina through a rotating optical wedge which causes the image to nutate on the surface in a regular pattern. As shown in Fig. 4–1, each photocell in the retina is connected to a flicker filter which compares the current state of the photocell to its state in the preceding time interval. If the state has changed, a pulse is generated. Timing is provided by a commutator geared to the motor driving the optical wedge.

The pulses from the flicker filters are combined in an *or*-gate and sent to a series of *and*-gates. Each gate is enabled for a particular segment of the nutation cycle by a signal from the commutator, with the result that the transform counters register the number of retina cell changes during a portion of the scan period. At the end of each scan cycle the data is processed by cyclically shifting the contents of the counters until the right-hand counter contains the minimum value, and then dividing the contents of each counter by this value to provide a descriptor which contains a "1" in the right hand position.

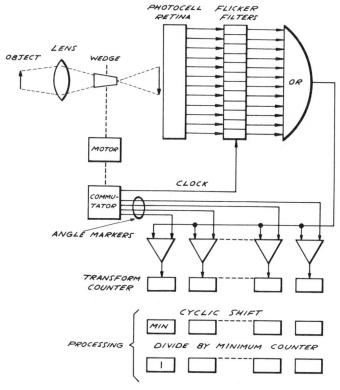

Figure 4–1. Principle of Chrysler optical processing scanner

The descriptor so formed has been found to be capable of discriminating between a number of different shapes and is apparently independent of character size, translation, and orientation (provided the image size is much larger than the individual retinal element). However, there are several shapes and characters which are indistinguishable with the simple processing scheme discussed and more complex processing rules must be developed.

## FROG'S RETINA

A model of a frog's retina using several levels of active components has been reported by Loebner.[18] It is constructed of opto-electronic panels arranged as shown in Fig. 4–2. Each panel consists of an array of opto-electronic devices,[19,28] which interact together in various ways to perform basic logical functions as well as more complex image processing

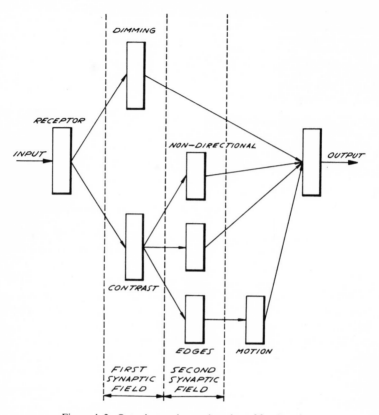

Figure 4–2. Optoelectronic panel analog of frog's retina

operations. It should be noted that the connections shown in the figure represent the passage of light between the panels and are not electrical conductors. Each optron consists of one or more CdS photodetectors and a ZnS electroluminescent emitter. By means of proper orientation and adjustment, these units can be made to exhibit optical switching, amplification, and storage. The combination shown has exhibited responses similar to those elicited by Lettvin, et al[17] (see Chapter 1).

## RCA PHONETIC TYPEWRITER

An example of a speech-recognition system is shown in principle in Fig. 4–3. Developed by RCA, it is called a *phonetic typewriter* since it responds to a spoken sound by typing out the printed equivalent.[22] The

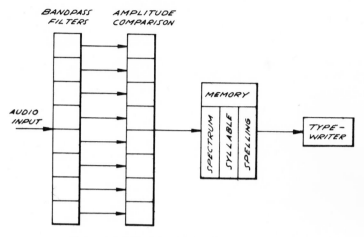

Figure 4-3. Principle of RCA phonetic typewriter

audio input representing the spoken sound is applied to a number of bandpass filters spanning the frequency range from 250 cycles to 10 kilocycles, which develop quantized frequency-amplitude-time functions. These functions are applied to comparison circuits which sharpen the significant features and form a descriptor which is compared with learned spectrum patterns stored in memory. Syllable information and an appropriate spelling are stored with the spectrum and can be presented to the typewriter for printout.

The machines built to date have only a limited vocabulary. Further development is necessary before a machine which is capable of responding to basic English speech can be built. The key probably lies in further probing of the sensor mechanisms themselves and of the data reduction processes in the brain. Since we have so much to learn from the natural world, let us quickly turn to some sensor principles which are based on logical, rather than biological, mechanisms.


## ARTIFICIAL SENSORS

A brute-force approach to pattern recognition yields little else than a large amount of data. For instance, if a visual field is divided by superimposing a mesh with 20 divisions per side, and the resulting squares are characterized as either black or white, $2^{400}$ possible patterns can be differentiated. This is approximately $10^{125}$. Now, if we assume that the smallest quantity of energy which can represent a bit of information is a quantum, it can be shown that a computer as large as the earth, having the same weight as the earth, and operating with natural quantum jumps which have occurred over the period of the earth's existence, could have processed no more than $10^{93}$ bits of information.[4] Even a complete listing of all of the possible patterns defined by this coarse matrix then is impossible. Simple subdivision of the visual field, therefore, is quite unlikely to succeed in a general purpose recognizer. Some form of sophisticated sensor system is necessary even for a recognition device of modest capability.

In view of the complexity of biological sensors, it is not surprising that there are many approaches to the design of artificial sensors. A glance at the proceedings of current symposia on the subject[9] shows that they range from simple one-to-one matching techniques, to intricate (theoretical) considerations of probability, variance, and correlation. As in building models of a biological neuron, in attempting to utilize biological sensor mechanisms we are hampered by the apparent intricacies and must search for simple logical implementations which retain the germ of the idea, but which sacrifice the finer subtleties for the sake of reduction to tangible hardware. The problem is to devise sensors which are compatible with the current state-of-the-art in electronic devices and logic which will respond to the *significant features* of the universe to be examined.

Fortunately, while the human brain and its sensors are called upon to respond to an infinite variety of situations, the functions of a pattern-recognition device can normally be limited to a relatively small universe in which recognition implies placing a particular event in one of a limited number of classes. For logical discrimination, all of the members of a particular class must be characterized by a certain set of features which are invariant. Conversely, members of different classes cannot contain exactly the same set of features.

The problem is to select the invariant class-determining features from all other features and to devise an efficient means for detecting their presence. These features should be independent of factors such as size, displacement, rotation, intensity, and background.[21] Once selected, the presence of a given set of features must be designated as representing a specific portion of the known environment.

Since much of the data used in today's world exists as printed or written material, it is inevitable that the major emphasis in pattern-recognition studies has been placed on visual data and more particularly on the recognition of letters, figures, and symbols. A great deal of work is concerned with the use of large digital computers in semimechanical analysis of letter patterns which have been reduced to a series of black or white squares by the superposition of a rectangular matrix. Various techniques are used to improve the quality of the image and to measure interrelationships between the figure areas. The complexity of these measures is limited only by the programmer's intuition. Many are quite successful in specific applications although they cannot be regarded as solutions to the general pattern-recognition problem for the reasons discussed earlier.[3,16]

## STATISTICAL DECISION MODELS

In Chapter 1, recognition was pictured as mapping a given set of parameters (features) onto a set of standard parameters. The standard set closest to the unknown set was then designated as describing the pattern presented. Provided certain a priori data is available, this operation can be implemented as shown in Fig. 4–4. The input pattern $v$ is to be mapped

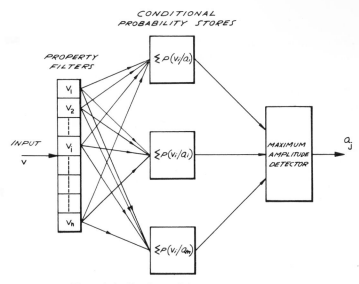

Figure 4–4. Simple conditional probability model

on to a set of standard patterns $a_1 \ldots a_m$ on the basis of certain features $v_1 \ldots v_n$ and a knowledge of the probability of the presence of a feature $v_l$ denoting that the input $v$ belongs to $a_i$. The presence of the component features is assumed to be detected by specific *property-filters,* and values of $P(v_i/a_i)$ are assumed to be part of the a priori data derived from standard patterns. The maximum amplitude detector observes the values accumulated for $P(v/a_i)$, i.e., $\Sigma P(v_i/a_i)$, and designates the input pattern in accordance with the highest probability.

More complex implementations of this principle using statistical decision theory[2] have been developed by Chow,[6] Marill and Green,[20] and more recently by Fu.[10] Rather than a parallel mechanism similar to the system of Fig. 4-4, Fu uses a sequential decision structure in which, after each decision, the operator is able to sample the confidence level of the classification and decide whether to accept this decision or whether to introduce more data.  In this way, large problems can be attacked piece-by-piece with a consequent reduction in hardware requirements, but at the expense of decision time.  The success of these techniques depends entirely on the ability of the experimenter to select the appropriate invariant features and to specify the conditional probabilities.

Pattern recognition, on the basis of decision functions, can be regarded as the act of selecting suitable partitioning functions in an $n$-dimensional hyperspace which contains vectors representing the individual patterns. Vectors separated by such functions fall into different categories.  Obviously, if the problem is relatively simple, and the vectors fall naturally into disjoint, simply connected, or convex regions, a high degree of separation (classification) can be obtained with linear functions (hyperplanes).[13]  If the problem is not simple, other techniques can be used, such as applying transformations to the vector space to improve the vector separability or the use of complex partitioning functions.[23]  A technique for partitioning the vector space by functions derived from the input patterns has been described.  In this case the degree of separation can be quite high since the partition functions do not necessarily have to fit classical forms.[24]

## PANDEMONIUM

A design for a general recognition network which is somewhat similar to that shown in Fig. 4-4 has been reported by Selfridge.[25]  Called *pandemonium,* it consists of several layers of elements designated as data, computational, cognitive and decision *demons* arranged as shown in Fig. 4-5. The system name is derived from the concept that the *cognitive demons* clamor for the attention of the *decision demon* in direct proportion to the perfection of the match between the input data and the data in the purview of each of the cognitive demons, thereby producing pandemonium.

The *data demons,* or sensors, convert the input pattern into digital form and pass the information on to the *computational demons,* which extract certain features.  In turn, this information is relayed to the cognitive demons, each of which has congizance of a given set of features and computes the degree of similarity between this set and those belonging to the input pattern.  That which has the closest match is selected by the decision demon as identifying the pattern presented.

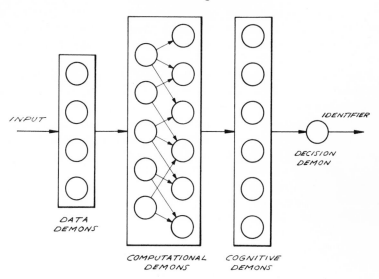

Figure 4–5. Pandemonium

The system can be made adaptive by providing variable weights within the computational network and in the interconnections between the computational and cognitive layers. A computer simulation which consists of six layers (input, clean up, inspection of features, comparison with learned feature distribution, computation of probabilities, and decision) has been used to identify handwritten characters.[8,26]

## RANDOM FEATURES

For reliable classification, as many significant features as possible should be used so that, even if each feature only contributes a minor amount of information towards the decision, taken together, they provide a positive indication of classification. In many practical cases, however, an analyst is hard pressed to define specific features and to compute their a priori probability of occurrence in a given environment. It would be a major step forward, therefore, if such features could be determined by electronic means.

Consider an environment containing $kr$ patterns, each of which is described by some combination of $n$ independent features. If the total number of patterns is to be divided into $k$ classifications, with $r$ signals per classification, then the first set of $r$ signals must be differentiated from $(k - 1)r$ signals, i.e., the number of decisions to be made is $r^2(k - 1)$. The second set of $r$ signals must be differentiated from $(k - 2)r$ signals, i.e., the number of decisions to be made is $r^2(k - 2)$, etc. Hence the total number of decisions which must be made to accomplish the desired classification is

$$d = r^2 \sum_{n=1}^{n=(k-1)} n, \qquad \text{i.e.,} \quad d = \frac{r^2 k(k - 1)}{2} \qquad (4.1)$$

Now, if the $n$ features have a random probability of being present in any particular pattern selected from the universe of patterns, the probability of any two patterns containing the same features is $1/2^n$, and the probability of two patterns being different is $1 - (1/2^n)$. Hence the probability of making successful decisions is

$$P = \left(1 - \frac{1}{2^n}\right)^d, \qquad (4.2)$$

so that, substituting from (4.1) and expanding for large values of $n$,

$$P = 1 - \frac{r^2 k(k - 1)}{2^{n+1}}. \qquad (4.3)$$

From this equation it is possible to compute the number of independent features ($n$) which must be present in a set of patterns to provide probability $P$ of being able to classify them into $k$ sets of $r$ patterns each.

If the probability of making an incorrect classification is $e$, and the number of classifications is large, (4.3) further reduces to

$$r^2 k^2 = e \cdot 2^{n+1} \qquad (4.4)$$

Hence for an error of 5 percent, when $n = 10$, $rk = 10$; when $n = 20$, $rk = 318$; when $n = 30$, $rk = 10^4$; etc. The values of $rk$ represent the total number of patterns under consideration. If only one pattern belongs to any class, $rk$ is the total number of classifications.

It should be noted that this analysis is concerned with the classification of patterns containing $n$ (unspecified) independent features randomly distributed within the group. If specific features are available, arranged in an optimum fashion, $n$ features will allow discrimination of $2^n$ selected patterns with complete certainty.

The concept of a random feature is particularly attractive and may be considered a general purpose technique. A priori knowledge of the patterns is not required. The only restrictions are that the features used be independent and that, for a given universe of patterns, each feature has a 50-percent chance of being *present*. Thus the method has wide application provided that there are $n$ such potential features in the group of patterns to be classified. Obviously, if we have 100 identical copies of a single photograph, there is no way to separate or distinguish them from one

another except by introducing additional data such as arbitrary number-
ing. Obviously, too, if all of the copies are identical, attempting to dif-
ferentiate one copy from the rest serves no useful purpose.

If the data to be classified can be converted to electrical signals, property filters can be used to develop signals which correspond to these *random features*. Thus, the signal developed by scanning a pattern can be
represented in hyperspace by a vector $S(t)$, which can be resolved along
a set of orthogonal axes into a number of independent components. This
is equivalent to the mathematical operation of *convolution*, i.e.,

$$C_n = \int_0^T F_n(T - t) \cdot S(t)dt \qquad (4.5)$$

where $C_n$ is the signal component along the $n$-axis and $F_n(t)$ is the $n^{\text{th}}$ of
a set of orthogonal functions. Many classical polynomial functions, such
as the polynomials of Laguerre, Legendre, Tchebychef, Hermite, and
Jacobi, display this property.[1,7,14] The selection of one or the other will influence the degree of separation which can be achieved between specific
signals.

Consider the network shown in Fig. 4–6. The input is assumed to be a
series of waveforms which are applied to $n$ parallel property filters, each
of which responds in some (different) way and provides a binary output.
The integrators perform the convolution operation between the incoming
signal and the orthogonal components. Their use has certain advantages
in that the effect of random noise which is of a much higher frequency
than the basic sampling function will be reduced significantly. For the
sake of providing a binary output, if the output of the integrator at time
$T$ is above the threshold level, the threshold detector generates a 1 signal;
if it is less than the threshold, the detector generates a 0. To ensure that
each filter has an equal probability of generating a 1 or a 0 so as to
achieve the best separation, it is necessary to select a threshold which is
the mean of the value of the orthogonal function within the period $T$.

If the filters are required to work against a particular environment,
their response can be improved by selection. In this way a certain amount
of preorganization (bias) can be injected into the system, thereby mim-
icking biological precedent. Thus, if, after a certain time in which a representative set of signals has been presented, no change (or little change)
has been observed in the output of one or more filters, the particular
orthogonal signal(s) associated with it can be replaced by others. If logic
for counting the changes at the output of the filters as a function of the
number of signals presented is included, filter adjustment can be made
automatic. The filter which has changed the least after presentation of a
certain number of signals is automatically given a new orthogonal signal,

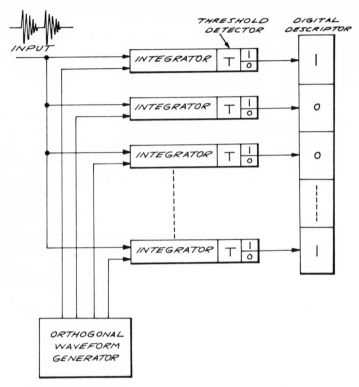

Figure 4–6. Implementation of general property filters

so that, after a number of trials, all of the filters will tend to about the same level of activity.

Consider the system shown in Fig. 4–7. The sensor bank is a set of property filters which develop a digital descriptor characteristic of the input. Initially, a set of training patterns is presented and the descriptors developed by the filters are stored in the model environment storage together with suitable digital identifiers.

After training, occurrence of an input signal produces a digital descriptor which is compared against the model environment for an exact fit or for agreement within certain distance limits (see Chapter 1). If it is sufficiently close to one of the standard words, the distance comparator develops an enable signal which opens the output gate and passes the appropriate *identity word* (identifier) to the output. If the unknown descriptor is not close to any of the descriptors contained in the model environment, the descriptor is passed to the unknown signal storage where it waits for the intervention of a human analyst to provide the correct identity. Once identified, the descriptor and identity words are trans-

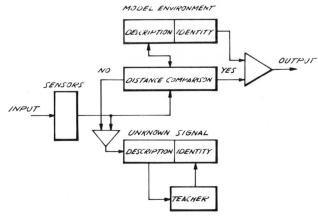

Figure 4–7. Use of learning system principles to classify data

ferred to the model environment so that later occurrences of this wave-
form can be typed automatically.

If the analyst's typing is assumed perfect, statistical decision elements
are not required, and the unknown *signal description–identity storage* can
be implemented with magnetic cores or a drum. If, however, the analyst
is unable to classify each signal with certainty, the unknown signal storage
can be expanded to include learning elements. Not until a high degree of
certainty has been established will the description-identity combination be
transferred to the model environment storage. A particular example of
this property filter technique, has been described by Fuhr.[11]

The problem of logical distance determination depends on the type of
sensors and on the general category of classification desired. If distance
is described as the *exclusive-or* of the descriptors taken term by term,
each digital bit of the descriptor word has equal weight. This is not necessarily desirable, particularly if the sampling functions are frequency-
dependent. In this case, in order to achieve a correspondence between
closeness of descriptors and actual input data, it may be necessary to
weight the bits. One way this can be done is to treat the descriptors as
binary words and take the arithmetic difference as a measure of closeness.

A refinement of the system of Fig. 4–7 which may improve identification is shown in Fig. 4–8. Here, the sensors are grouped in three sections.
The first group might be devoted to low-frequency phenomena and the
third group might be devoted to high-frequency phenomena. By differencing on the three segments of the descriptor in parallel, it is possible to ob-
tain a better comparison without the logical distance mis-match in one
area being compensated by closeness in another.

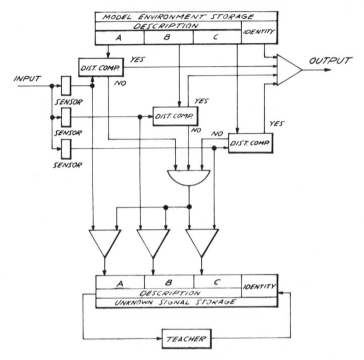

Figure 4-8. A more sophisticated classifying system, using significant descriptor components to provide a better comparison with the model environment

An alternative scheme which uses a learning element such as madaline is shown in Fig. 4-9. Here the threshold elements are used to generalize the output of the random features property filter bank so as to provide a coded output of the number of classifications. As a minimum, the number of outputs (and hence the number of threshold elements) is $\log_2 k$. Training is accomplished by the presentation of standard patterns, adjustment of the orthogonal functions generator to achieve approximately the same levels of activity in all filters, and adjustment of the adaline input weights to achieve suitable output codes for the individual classifications. It is important that the filters be properly adjusted before any attempt is made to establish the response of the madaline network.

## THRESHOLD DEVICES

As mentioned in Chapter 2, adaline networks (madalines) and perceptrons have both been trained to classify patterns. Although they are adaptive, and the decision function(s) can be adjusted on a trial-and-

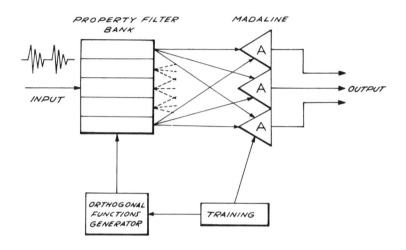

Figure 4-9. Recognition device using randomly selected features and Madaline

error basis, they can only perform satisfactorily when the vectors are easily separable.[15] Most of the work has been based on the use of a rectangular matrix of photocells as shown in Fig. 2–22, with the individual cells providing a binary input to the adalines or associator units of the perceptron. Provided the input data is presented in the same manner each time, i.e., same orientation and size, these devices are able to classify within the limits of the linearly separable functions.[12] Changes in size, orientation, and background generally require retraining, although some generalization is apparently performed by the back-coupled perceptron and certain of the multilayer networks. Without more sophisticated sensor equipment, it is doubtful if better performance can be anticipated.

## PREDICTION

The penny-matching example discussed in Chapter 3 is also a demonstration of a form of pattern recognition. Here the problem is not to classify a single event, but to determine any bias over a series of events (i.e., the pattern is time-dependent) and to predict the next event on this basis. Such prediction will be successful only if there is some well-behaved connection between related events. If a sequence of events is represented as ... $(N - 2)$, $(N - 1)$, $(N)$, $(N + 1)$, $(N + 2)$ ... etc., where $(N)$ signifies the present; $(N - 2)$, $(N - 1)$ signify the past (history); and $(N + 1)$, $(N + 2)$ signify the future, then, for a deterministic process we may postulate some functional relationship between these events. Thus,

$$F_0 = \frac{(N)}{(N + 1)}$$

$$F_1 = \frac{(N - 1)}{(N + 1)} \qquad (4.6)$$

$$F_2 = \frac{(N - 2)}{(N + 1)}, \text{ etc.}$$

These relationships can be learned by a system such as shown in Fig. 4–10.

Successive events are stored in the registers shown in the upper left-hand corner of the diagram. Initially only the present event $(N)$ and the two preceding events $(N - 1)$, $(N - 2)$ are present. Each is applied to a separate learning network which develops (predicts) the imminent event

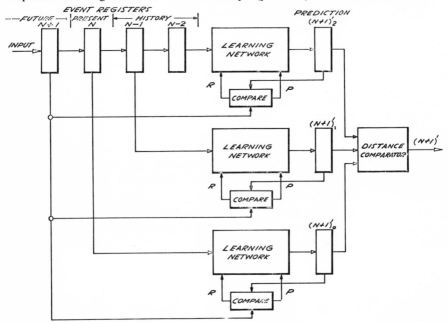

Figure 4–10. A simple predictor

($N$ + 1). These predictions are then compared and an output is generated which represents the most likely value of ($N$ + 1). It may be equal to the component predictions $(N + 1)'_0$, $(N + 1)'_1$, $(N + 1)'_2$ if they are the same (a not very likely state of affairs), to two of them, or to some simple (or weighted) average of the components. In fact, the distance comparator might also be a learning network.

Upon the occurrence of event ($N$ + 1), it is entered in the ($N$ + 1) register and compared with the predicted values generated by each network. Appropriate reward and punishment signals are developed by the individual comparators and the learning network connectives are adjusted accordingly. As soon as this process is completed, the events are shifted to their proper places in the register chain and the estimate for the next event is formed. Obviously, the prediction can be based on as many, or as few, terms as desired, and they do not necessarily have to be successive terms. In many processes, events depend primarily upon the immediately past events, so that the prediction network becomes quite simple.

An example of a system of this type which may be used to perform *data compaction* is shown in Fig. 4–11. Such a function can be of considerable value for indicating events which vary from the normal, and for reducing the amount of data to be transmitted over a telemetry link (for instance). The process of prediction is performed as described previously. If $(N + 1)' = (N + 1)$, this event is not transmitted since it can be reconstructed at any time in the future by the use of a similar predictor. If

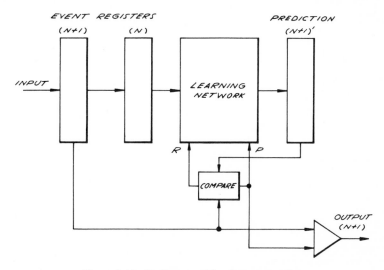

Figure 4-11. Predictor used for data compaction

$(N + 1)' \neq (N + 1)$, the event is transmitted since it varies sufficiently from the structure of previous events that it is not predicted by the learning network on the basis of previous experience, and therefore may be of considerable significance. By employing such a device to process data before transmission over a data link, the sending of redundant messages can be avoided. If required, the complete message can be reconstructed at the receiver (or at some later point) by using a similar network.

## IDEAL PATTERN RECOGNIZER

Although not all of the parts are currently available to build a general purpose pattern recognizer, it is possible to propose a concept which in corporates some of the principles described in this book. The first problem is to provide a sufficient data processing capability to reduce the environment to its significant features and then to provide a classifier which is truly general purpose and not limited in the ways in which it can divide the function space. A further very desirable function would be the automatic generation of identifiers for new signals. In principle all of this is possible with the system shown in Fig. 4–12.

In practice, the physical implementation of the various subsystems introduces constraints which rapidly degrade the performance. Ignoring these for the moment, signals from the environment impinge on various sensors $(1, 2 \ldots N)$ some of which may be designed to detect the presence of particular features, and some of which are trainable so that they separate specific patterns. The latter may include random feature property filters.

The data developed by the sensors is digitalized and entered in the (descriptor) register. Initially, during the training cycle, the model environment is empty (or nearly so) so that no valid comparison can be made in the distance comparator. The data is therefore transmitted to the learning network and the goal network which attempt to form an appropriate identifier. A teacher, on the basis of observing the environment, recognizing the data to be classified, and knowing the proper identifier, repeatedly rewards or punishes the goal network until it directs the learning network to form the correct identifier. It is assumed that the learning networks are able to form at least as many logical connectives as are required by this task.

When the correct identifier has been formed (as signified by the teacher) both the descriptor and identifier are gated to appropriate storage locations in the model environment. In addition, the identifier is entered into a code conversion table, where it is matched with instructions for the

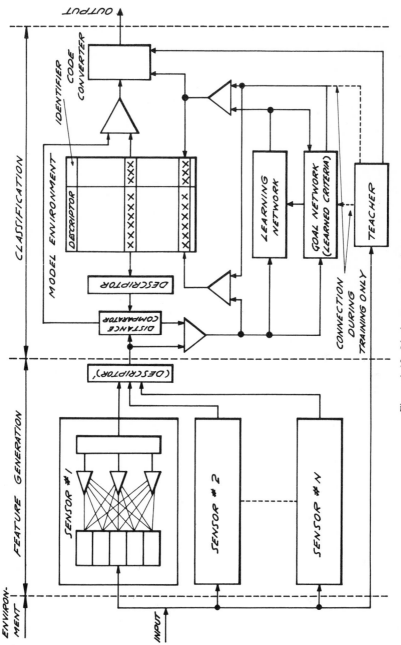

Figure 4–12. Ideal pattern recognizer

printout, say, of a description in English of the pattern recognized. A tenuous similarity may be seen between the learning of the identifier and the establishing of memory trace. Once learned, the *trace* is placed in storage for easy recall.

When the training period is completed (including adjustment of the sensors) the system is ready to receive its first unrehearsed pattern. If the distance comparator is able to find a match in the environment storage ($\pm$ permissible distance), the appropriate identifier is gated to the code converter and an intelligible identification is generated. If the distance comparator is unable to achieve a match, the pattern is outside of the training limits and the descriptor is sent to the learning network. Here an identifier is generated under the control of the goal network and is placed in an empty storage location in the model environment with the descriptor. On the next occurrence of a similar input, the distance comparator will be successful in establishing a match, and the identifier will be sent to the code converter. At some time the teacher must supply an intelligible description to convert the identifier to an understandable symbol. This is akin to the learning period in a human, during which we may recognize certain shapes or forms and may assign some made-up word to describe them to ourselves, although it is not until some wiser (or more knowing) individual provides us with the generally accepted name, that we can converse intelligibly about our observation.

Several factors affect the performance of such a system. They are essentially the basic limitations which have been recognized throughout our discussion.

1. The sensors must operate on significant features, which are provided by the designer or which are within the span of the trainable filters.
2. The bits which form the composite descriptor must be of equal weight or have a fixed relation one to another for the operation of distancing to be effective.
3. All known significant patterns must be described in terms of digital descriptors which are separated by at least twice the distance tolerance.
4. The trainable goal network must have some generalizing capability, otherwise $2^n$ patterns (or the total pattern environment) will be required to train it to perform properly.

Thus, although the principles are not unduly difficult, the practical implementation of such a system may be beyond our abilities for some time to come.

## DISCUSSION

The incorporation of complex preprocessing in the sensor field is the key to the development of any successful recognition system. The only proven general purpose device is man himself, and much remains to be done before we have even a first-order approximation of the organization of the sensory inputs to the central nervous system. Without such knowledge, a recognizer for any but the most specialized tasks appears to be beyond the present state-of-the-art. Statistical decision theory or the generation of random features are very poor substitutes for biological mechanisms which may have developed over millions of years.

For particular tasks, however, such as character recognition or signal processing, in which the environment is restricted to a relatively small section of all possible patterns, the artificial sensor mechanisms described have a reasonable probability of success. The secret is to concentrate on the specific limited objective and to ignore all extraneous materials. This calls for a thorough understanding of the problem and a keen analytical approach to the selection of significant features, or the utilization of sampling functions.

Should a general adaptive recognition system be constructed at some later date, it is not outside the realm of possibility that it will allow the development of a whole family of special purpose systems based on the principles learned. Such systems would not incorporate learning elements, but would rather duplicate the learned states of the elements in the original system. In this way much of the electronic complexity of a learning system can be dispensed with to provide special tools for specific tasks. The learning system then becomes a *designer*.

The work discussed has been concerned with so-called *noncooperative systems,* i.e. ones in which the pattern to be identified is not constrained to be part of a small class, but rather may contain any number of features. Work concerned with *cooperative systems* has been neglected since this does not really seem to fall within the scope of learning systems. Such systems are, however, beginning to play a major role in modern society. For instance, most of us are only too well aware of the standardized symbols which appear on bank checks for the purpose of recording our account number and bank identification. These characters have been designed for (almost) faultless reading by a variety of devices using matching (masking) techniques. Since the type font and location of the imprint are tightly controlled, reliable performance can be obtained at a reasonable price. Other examples of these types of cooperating patterns (characters) are seen on credit cards and various automatic billing systems. But for the fact that the imprint is relatively easy to read, and can be used in *human-to-human* transactions, it is really little better than the familiar holes used in punched cards.

## REFERENCES

1. M. Abramowitz and I. A. Stegun, *Handbook of Mathematical Functions* (National Bureau of Standards Applied Mathematics Series, no. 55), U.S. Government Printing Office, Washington, D.C., 1964, pp. 771–802.

2. T. W. Anderson, *An Introduction to Multivariate Statistical Analysis,* John Wiley, New York, 1958.

3. J. S. Bomba, "Alpha-Numeric Character Recognition Using Local Operations," *Proceedings, Eastern Joint Computer Conference (AFIPS),* 1959, pp. 218–224.

4. H. J. Bremermann, "Optimization Through Evolution and Recombination," *Self-Organizing Systems—1962,* M. C. Yovitts, G. T. Jacobi, and G. D. Goldstein, eds., Spartan Books, Washington, D.C., 1962, pp. 93–106.

5. D. N. Buell, "Chrysler Optical Processing Scanner," *Proceedings, Eastern Joint Computer Conference, (AFIPS),* 1961, pp. 352–370.

6. C. K. Chow, "An Optimum Character Recognition System Using Decision Functions," *IRE Transactions on Electronic Computers,* vol. EC-6, 1957, pp. 247–254.

7. E. U. Condon and H. Odishaw, eds., *Handbook of Physics,* McGraw-Hill, New York, 1958, pp. 1/49–1/52.

8. W. Doyle, "Recognition of Sloppy, Hand-Printed Characters," *Proceedings, Western Joint Computer Conference (AFIPS),* 1960, pp. 132–142.

9. G. L. Fischer, D. K. Pollock, B. Raddack, and M. E. Stevens, eds., *Optical Character Recognition,* Spartan Books, Washington, D.C., 1962.

10. K. S. Fu, "A Sequential Decision Model for Optimum Recognition," *Biological Prototypes and Synthetic Systems,* E. E. Bernard and M. R. Kare, eds., Plenum Press, New York, 1962, vol. 1, pp. 270–277.

11. W. H. Fuhr, "The Use of Random Property Filters and Learning Networks for Signal Recognition," paper presented at *Second Bionics Symposium,* Air Force Systems Command, Wright-Patterson AFB, Ohio, 1963. To be published.

12. J. K. Hawkins, "Self-Organizing Systems—A Review and Commentary," *Proceedings, IRE,* vol. 49, 1961, pp. 31–48.

13. W. H. Highleyman, "Linear Decision Functions with Application to Pattern Recognition," *Proceedings, IRE,* vol. 50, 1962, pp. 1501–1514.

14. W. H. Huggins, "Signal Theory," *IRE Transactions on Circuit Theory,* vol. CT-3, 1956, pp. 210–216.

15. H. Kazmierczak and K. Steinbuch, "Adaptive Systems in Pattern Recognition," *IEEE Transactions on Electronic Computers,* vol. EC-12, 1963, pp. 822–835.

16. R. A. Kirsch, C. Ray, L. Cahn and G. H. Urban, "Experiments in Processing Pictorial Information with a Digital Computer," *Proceedings, Eastern Joint Computer Conference (AFIPS),* 1957, pp. 221–229.

17. J. Y. Lettvin, H. Maturana, W. S. McCulloch, and W. Pitts, "What the Frog's Eye Tells the Frog's Brain," *Proceedings, IRE,* vol. 47, 1959, pp. 1940–1951.

18. E. E. Loebner, "Image Processing and Functional Retina Synthesis," *Bionics Symposium,* WADD Technical Report 60-600, 1960, pp. 309–338.

19. _____, "Opto-Electronic Devices and Networks," *Proceedings, IRE,* vol. 43, 1955, pp. 1897–1906.

20. T. Marill and D. M. Green, "Statistical Recognition Functions and the Design of Pattern Recognizers," *IRE Transactions on Electronic Computers,* vol. EC-9, 1960, pp. 472–477.

21. M. Minsky, "Steps Toward Artificial Intelligence," *Proceedings, IRE,* vol. 49, 1961, pp. 8–30.

22. F. J. Olsen and H. Belar, "Recognition of the Spoken Word by Machine," *Biological Prototypes and Synthetic Systems,* E. E. Bernard and M. R. Kare, eds., Plenum Press, New York, 1962, vol. 1, pp. 110–118.

23. G. Sebestyen, *Decision Making Processes in Pattern Recognition,* Macmillan, New York, 1962.

24. _____, "Pattern Recognition by an Adaptive Process of Sample Set Construction," *IRE Transactions on Information Theory,* vol. IT-8-5, September 1962, pp. 5-82 to 5-91.

25. O. G. Selfridge, "Pandemonium: A Paradigm for Learning," *Mechanization of Thought Processes,* Her Majesty's Stationery Office, London, 1959, vol. 1, pp. 513–526.

26. _____ and U. Neisser, "Pattern Recognition by Machine," *Scientific American,* vol. 203, August 1960, pp. 60–68.

27. M. E. Stevens, "Abstract Shape Recognition by Machine," *Proceedings, Eastern Joint Computer Conference (AFIPS),* 1961, pp. 332–351.

28. J. R. Biard, E. L. Bonin, W. T. Matzen, and J. D. Merryman, "Optoelectronics as Applied to Functional Electronic Blocks," *Proceedings, IEEE,* vol. 52, 1964, pp. 1529–1536.

Chapter 5

# PROGRAMMING

As discussed in Chapter 1, the second attribute which would greatly improve the performance of a computer would be an ability to construct programs from general instructions provided by the analyst so as to relieve him of the burdensome job of preparing the detailed program steps and, perhaps, to enable the machine to solve problems for which the analyst has no ready answer. Filling in the program skeleton with routine steps is mostly a matter of replacing the knowledge of the analyst by a set of rules and instructions (albeit a rather large set) in computer language. However, having the computer utilize its internal capability to solve problems for which no complete program skeleton exists is much more difficult. It requires the simulation of intelligent behavior.

In the same way that the development of a satisfactory general purpose recognizer apparently requires detailed study of the biological sensor mechanisms, the development of a satisfactory *heuristic* programming technique requires an understanding of the philosophical and psychological processes of the human mind and of how we approach problem solving. Since psychologists apparently do not agree on a theory of the human intellectual processes, we must do as best we can with the mathematical techniques and observational faculties afforded us.

Since the models described in the previous chapters can be simulated on a digital computer, they may be said to provide a heuristic capability. However, such an arrangement is equivalent to providing the machine with an algorithm for solving certain classes of problems, and does not develop an intrinsic programming capability.[4]

This is not to discredit such practices, since it is often much simpler and cheaper to use an available computer to simulate a system design than it is to build a special purpose piece of hardware. Changes in design can be made rapidly, and a great variety of problems can be tested in a relatively short time. This flexibility allows the operator to design and redesign the system on the basis of its behavior and the computer becomes, essentially, an experimental tool for system development.

## ASSEMBLERS AND COMPILERS

The art of program writing has assumed more and more importance as computer designs have become (somewhat) standardized, as modular construction techniques (using standard circuits) have been perfected, and as machines have become larger. In the beginning, the problem was to design and build circuits which would perform satisfactorily for even a short time; to develop novel mechanical assemblies for input, output, and storage devices; and to evolve a general purpose system organization. With the perfection of germanium and silicon diodes and transistors, magnetic cores, printed circuits, and the like, and with designs tempered by the experience of building many different machines, computer hardware has reached the stage where failures are uncommon. Even in the rugged environment of a rocket or a future spaceship, modern-day computers can be relied on to operate (almost) infallibly and the computing capacity available in a moderate amount of space is now equal to all but the largest of problems.

It is the program writing which is the major part of any new computer development and the money invested in the preparation of the *software* may often exceed that which is committed to the development of the *hardware*. Of course, so large an effort results in user convenience, for it is generally comitted to the writing of complex translator programs which allow the machine to be controlled by quasi-English instructions. Although these programs are not produced by mechanical learning systems, the principle involved is very much that of a large trainable network in which the analyst provides the algorithms for the production of the necessary connectives.

The first such programs were called *assemblers.* They are able to respond to instructions such as "multiply" and "divide" (or rather the mnemonic codes for these instructions) and to produce the proper machine coding for these operations. In general there is a one-to-one correspondence between the symbolic (mnemonic) codes of the assembler and the machine instructions produced. Later programs, called *compilers,* are able to respond to much more powerful instruction codes and to produce a sequence of machine operations in response to a single statement.[14]

Consider the problem of determining $y$ for given values of $x$ in the expression:

$$y = (ax^2 + b), \tag{5.1}$$

where $a$ and $b$ are constants, and $x = x_0(c)x_n$. Each term can be worked out in a matter of seconds by a competent technician using a slide rule. To write and prove a machine program for this equation will require much more time. Once written, however, the program will allow the computer to produce results very rapidly for virtually any number of values of $x$, and with consistent accuracy. The steps in the programming task are as follows:

1. Become familiar with the capabilities of the computer to be used. The word length, number of registers, the input/output equipment available and the type of storage will play a significant part in optimizing the procedure.
2. Prepare a clear, concise, umambiguous statement of the problem including the magnitudes of the input parameters and the expected answer. Unless the problem is stated in this manner, the answer obtained will probably be incorrect.
3. Evaluate the various techniques which may be used to reduce the problem to elementary numerical steps. For instance, trigonometric functions can be derived by interpolation between values stored in a look-up table, or by substitution in a Taylor series; differentiation is very nearly the same as differencing; etc.
4. Prepare a detailed flow chart showing each step which the computer must make in developing the solution to the problem.
5. Allocate machine resources to each operation, i.e., storage locations, input/output equipment, etc.
6. Write instructions for the computation in machine code.
7. Prepare punched cards, punched paper tape, or other media which contain the instructions written above.
8. Load program into machine.
9. Test program functioning with specially prepared examples.
10. Correct program.
11. Solve problem.
12. Prepare description of program for use by others.

The significant registers, storage locations, and control functions of a small digital computer (based on Control Data Corporation 160A) are shown in Fig. 5–1. A flow diagram for the problem as it would be executed by the machine is shown in Fig. 5–2, and the program written with the aid of an assembler (OSAS) is shown in Fig. 5–3. In addition to the assembler mnemonic codes, the listing includes the programmer's explanation of the steps and the machine code equivalent. Since our purpose is to illustrate the magnitude of the programming problem and the reduction in human effort effected by a compiler, rather than to teach the

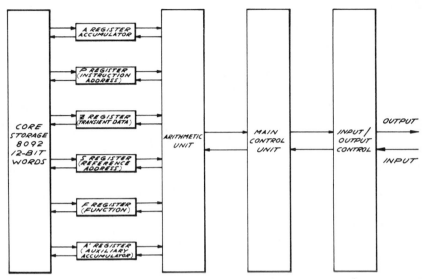

Figure 5-1. Primary CDC 160A computer used to compute $Y = AX^2 + B_n$

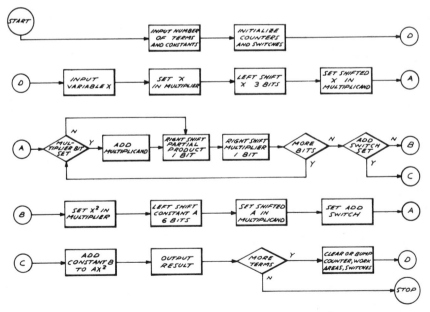

Figure 5-2.   OSAS flow chart for computation of $y = ax^2 + b$ for $x_0(c)x_n$

| MACHINE PROGRAM | | OSAS ASSEMBLER PROGRAM | | | PROGRAMMER'S COMMENTS |
|---|---|---|---|---|---|
| | 0000 | | bnk0 | | osas assembler example |
| | 0000 | | org | 0 | |
| 0000 | 7101 | | jfi | 1 | |
| 0001 | 0100 | | | start | |
| | 0020 | | org | 20 | |
| 0020 | 0000 | mucand | | 0 | multiplicand |
| 0021 | 0000 | mulier | | 0 | multiplier |
| 0022 | 0000 | pprdct | | 0 | partial product |
| 0023 | 0000 | trmctr | | 0 | number of terms |
| 0024 | 0000 | aconst | | 0 | constant a |
| 0025 | 0000 | bconst | | 0 | constant b |
| 0026 | 0000 | xvarbl | | 0 | variable x |
| 0027 | 0000 | result | | 0 | result |
| 0030 | 0000 | bitctr | | 0 | operand size |
| 0031 | 0000 | mudone | | 0 | add switch |
| | 0100 | | org | 100 | |
| 0100 | 0060 | start | sid0 | | entrance |
| 0101 | 7500 | | exc | 4102 | |
| 0102 | 4102 | | | | |
| 0103 | 7600 | | ina | | input number of terms |
| 0104 | 6401 | | zjb | 1 | |
| 0105 | 1600 | | scc | 7777 | |
| 0106 | 7777 | | | | |
| 0107 | 4023 | | std | trmctr | set term counter |
| 0110 | 7600 | | ina | | input constant a |
| 0111 | 4024 | | std | aconst | |
| 0112 | 7600 | | ina | | input constant b |
| 0113 | 4025 | | std | bconst | |
| 0114 | 0400 | nxttrm | ldn | 0 | |
| 0115 | 4031 | | std | mudone | clear add switch |
| 0116 | 7600 | | ina | | input variable x |
| 0117 | 4026 | | std | xvarbl | |
| 0120 | 4021 | | std | mulier | set multiplier |
| 0121 | 0110 | | ls3 | | |
| 0122 | 4020 | | std | mucand | set shifted multiplicand |
| 0123 | 0503 | | lcn | 3 | |
| 0124 | 4030 | | std | bitctr | set operand size |
| 0125 | 0400 | muply1 | ldn | 0 | |
| 0126 | 4022 | | std | pprdct | clear partial product |
| 0127 | 2021 | muply2 | ldd | mulier | |
| 0130 | 0201 | | lpn | 1 | |
| 0131 | 6003 | | zjf | noadd | multiplier bit set |
| 0132 | 2020 | | ldd | mucand | |
| 0133 | 5022 | | rad | pprdct | add shifted multiplicand |
| 0134 | 2022 | noadd | ldd | pprdct | |
| 0135 | 0114 | | rs1 | | shift partial product |
| 0136 | 4022 | | std | pprdct | |
| 0137 | 2021 | | ldd | mulier | |
| 0140 | 0114 | | rs1 | | shift multiplier |
| 0141 | 4021 | | std | mulier | |

| MACHINE PROGRAM | | OSAS ASSEMBLER PROGRAM | | | PROGRAMMER'S COMMENTS |
|---|---|---|---|---|---|
| 0142 | 5430 | | aod | bitctr | |
| 0143 | 6514 | | nzb | muply2 | |
| 0144 | 2031 | | ldd | mudone | |
| 0145 | 6113 | | nzf | add | j to add |
| 0146 | 2024 | | ldd | aconst | start second multiply |
| 0147 | 0111 | | 1s6 | | |
| 0150 | 4020 | | std | mucand | set shifted multiplicand |
| 0151 | 2022 | | ldd | pprdct | |
| 0152 | 4021 | | std | mulier | set multiplier |
| 0153. | 0506 | | lcn | 6 | |
| 0154 | 4030 | | std | bitctr | set operand size |
| 0155 | 5431 | | aod | mudone | set add switch |
| 0156 | 7101 | | jfi | 1 | |
| 0157 | 0125 | | | muply1 | j to second multiply |
| 0160 | 2025 | add | ldd | bconst | |
| 0161 | 5022 | | rad | pprdct | add constant b |
| 0162 | 4027 | | std | result | |
| 0163 | 7500 | | exc | 4104 | |
| 0164 | 4104 | | | | |
| 0165 | 2027 | | ldd | result | |
| 0166 | 7677 | | ota | | punch result |
| 0167 | 5423 | | aod | trmctr | |
| 0170 | 6005 | | zjf | done | more terms |
| 0171 | 7500 | | exc | 4102 | |
| 0172 | 4102 | | | | |
| 0173 | 7101 | | jfi | 1 | |
| 0174 | 0114 | | | nxttrm | j to solve next term |
| 0175 | 7700 | done | hlt | | |
| | 0000 | | | end | |

Figure 5-3. Program to compute $y = ax^2 + b$ written for CDC 160A computer and OSAS assembler.

rudiments of the subject, we will not dwell on the detailed explanation of these figures.

Instead, let us compare this large amount of work (for a relatively simple problem) with that which is required to compute the same problem on the same machine provided with a compiler. Figure 5-4 shows the same program written for use with a CDC 160A and FORTRAN compiler (a computer language developed by the International Business Machines Corporation). In this case the symbolic inputs are transformed into the machine-coded program of Fig. 5-3 by appropriate instructions contained within the compiler program. Even a cursory glance shows that the task is reduced by an order of magnitude. Moreover the FORTRAN program automatically accommodates nonintegral values and values which may exceed the computer word length. The program of Fig. 5-3 cannot cope with these situations without modification.

| FORTRAN PROGRAM | | PROGRAMMER'S COMMENTS |
|---|---|---|
| c | fortran compiler example | |
| 1 | format (f10.0) | define input format |
| 2 | format (e14.8/) | define output format |
| | read 1, t | input number of terms |
| | n = t | convert to fixed point |
| | read 1, a,b | input constants |
| | do 3 m = 1,n | set up loop |
| | read 1, x | input variable |
| | y = a*x**2.0 + b | solve equation |
| 3 | punch 2, y | output result |
| | stop | |
| 4 | end | |
| | end | |

Figure 5-4. Program to compute $y = ax^2 + b$ written for CDC 160A and FORTRAN compiler.

Thus the tedious machine codes, or mnemonic codes of the assembler, are replaced by quasi-English statements. The language is not difficult to learn and yet is sufficiently powerful that an engineer, scientist, mathematician, or businessman can use it to solve his particular problems without spending valuable time in tedious program preparation.

The same problem can be solved by programs written in any number of symbolic languages. A given computer will provide identical answers provided the proper compiler is used. Further, using the same instructions (statements), the problem can be solved on different machines (perhaps manufactured by competing companies and incorporating unique principles) without regard to their internal characteristics (again, provided the proper compiler is used). A compiler, therefore, removes the programmer from close association with a specific machine (except for the basic consideration of machine capacity), provides a semiautomatic capability for program preparation; and makes it possible to develop the concept of a programming language which does not depend on hardware organization.[8,17]

A compiler provides the link between instructions written in a specific language and their implementation on a given computer. The connectives in the compiler program are generated by well-qualified analysts who work out each step in complete detail. While the same language compilers for different machines use a common set of input instructions (FORTRAN, for instance), the idiosyncrasies of the organization of the machines are woven into the detail, and the outputs can be expected to be quite different unless the proper compilers are used. A separate compiler program *must* be written for each machine.

## HEURISTIC TECHNIQUES

*Heuristic programs* contain as much information as the programmer can provide concerning the specifics of the problem to be solved, together with some logical rules for optimizing the chance of success at intermediate points in the computation. Unlike the programs just discussed, heuristic programs are not a complete series of statements which guarantee the solution to a problem because the programmer has discovered the universal rules governing every possible set of situations. Rather the problem is normally defined only in general terms and the path to the solution has to be developed by the computer. Most likely, this path will be different each time the problem is run.

*Heuristic program writing* is an attempt to endow a computer with the information an intelligent human would use as he gropes his way through a particular problem. Therefore it is based on whatever knowledge we have of what a well-informed, alert individual may require in order to proceed to a result. The basic work in this speciality has been developed from the study of games (such as tic-tac-toe, checkers, and chess) which are relatively complex, but which at any particular stage in the game can be specified precisely. The goal is to win, using the rules of play provided. In this sense, games are quite artificial and are a far cry from the more usual social or political situation in which we may not have a precise definition of a win, and the rules can be changed unilaterally at the whim of one of the participants. Under these circumstances, the most important objective may be not to lose. Nevertheless, games provide a convenient starting point and allow us to devise programming schemes for well-ordered situations, which can be modified later.

## TIC-TAC-TOE

To illustrate some of the principles of heuristic program development, consider a game of tic-tac-toe between players $A$ and $B$. For convenience, the positions in the $3 \times 3$ matrix will be identified as shown in Fig. 5–5. Initially, $A$ has the choice of nine squares, although, in fact, there are only three unique positions available. (Because of the symmetry, squares 11, 13, 31, and 33 are equivalent; and squares 12, 21, 23, and 32 are equivalent.) In reply, $B$ can select any one of the eight remaining positions; $A$ will then take one of the remaining seven locations, and so on, until one player has won, or they have drawn. There are a total of 9! (i.e., 362,880) sequences of nine plays which can be made to fill the matrix. However, the total number of possible games is less than this since only five plays

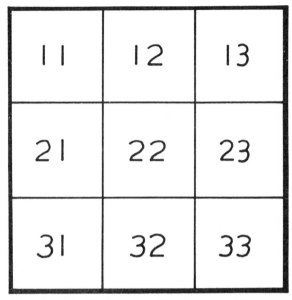

Figure 5–5. Identification of positions for game of tic-tac-toe

are necessary for *A* to win. If we assume that *A* and *B* play randomly, an average game may require six or seven plays. Thus there are between $9!/3!$ and $9!/2!$ (i.e., approximately 100,000) possible games.

The sequence of plays can be represented in the fashion of the tree[9] shown in Fig. 5–6. In the first play, *A* can select any one of the nine squares. In the second play, *B* can select any one of the remaining eight squares. This is symbolized by connecting each designator in the first column to eight designators in the second column representing the remaining locations. In all, 72 designations ($9 \times 8$) should be listed in the second column. Similarly each of the 72 designators should be connected to 7 designators in the third column, etc. Carried to its limit, such a tree would represent all possible games. For the sake of brevity, suppose *A* selected square 22 in the first play. Figure 5–6 shows this position connected to the eight possible locations which *B* can select in the second play. If *B* selects location 11, the list in the upper portion of column 3 represents the plays from which *A* may now select, and so on. In all, three specific games are shown—a small fraction of the possible total.

One way of programming a computer to play tic-tac-toe is to have the entire game tree stored in memory and to instruct the machine to examine all the possible plays it can make on the basis of the likelihood of winning. At each step, this would require searching all possible future

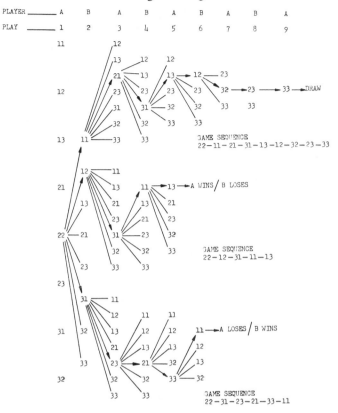

Figure 5-6. Decision trees for three games of tic-tac-toe

steps in the game to determine which one of the possible immediate plays is connected to the most wins. If two or more possible plays have the same probability of success, a further search might be made of the subsequent branches to see which of them has the highest probability of producing a draw. Alternatively, the search could be made on the basis of which of the possible moves has the least probability of allowing the opponent to win.

If the computer plays first, this mode of operation would require searching some 100,000 games in order to compute the probability of success associated with each square. (With some sophistication in the manner of search to take advantage of symmetry, this number can be reduced appreciably.) In reply to the opponent's first selection (second play), the machine would then have to search some 1,700 possible continuations (assuming an average game); and for its third selection (fifth play), the machine would have to search a further 40 continuations.

While the magnitude of the later searches is hardly significant compared to the first, the overall technique is obviously cumbersome and time-consuming. For anything more complex than tic-tac-toe, the complete tree-search technique is out of the question.

Another way of programming a computer to play tic-tac-toe is to allow the machine to continually optimize its chance of winning. No attempt is made to search forward in the game tree beyond the consequences of the immediate play. Thus the computer may ask a series of questions such as:

1. Is there any single location presently unoccupied which, in conjunction with two positions already filled by the computer, will form a sequence of three? That is, in the individual sequences below

$$
\left.
\begin{array}{l}
11, 12, 13 \\
21, 22, 23 \\
31, 32, 33 \\
11, 21, 31 \\
12, 22, 32 \\
13, 23, 33 \\
11, 22, 33 \\
13, 22, 31
\end{array}
\right\} \quad \text{Win Matrix}
$$

   are any two positions occupied by the computer where the third position is unoccupied?
2. Is there any single location presently unoccupied which, in conjunction with two positions already filled by the opponent, will form a sequence of three in the win matrix?
3. Is there an unoccupied location which is common to four winning sequences (i.e., is 11, 13, 31, or 33 unoccupied)?
4. Is there an unoccupied location which is common to three winning sequences (i.e., is 11, 13, 31, or 33 unoccupied)?
5. Is there an unoccupied location which is common to two winning sequences (i.e., 12, 21, 23, or 32 unoccupied)?

The first two questions determine whether the computer has an immediate chance to win or to prevent the opponent from winning. Questions 3, 4, and 5 provide a simple logic for the selection of a location if questions 1 and 2 are answered negatively. By putting them together in the sequence shown in Fig. 5–7, it is possible to provide the computer with a capability to play to win or draw but not lose.

The rules do not specify completely all situations since it is possible to

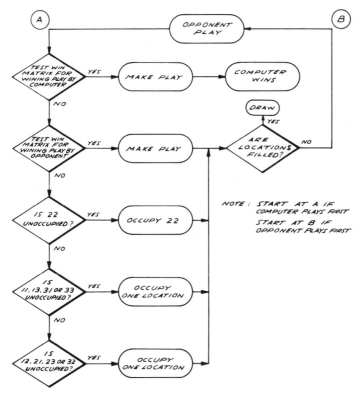

Figure 5-7. Flow diagram for tic-tac-toe

choose at random between competing locations in questions 4 and 5. However, the start is well-defined (questions 3 or 4) and the ending is specified (questions 1 or 2). A greater degree of freedom is obtained if just the first two questions are used so that only the ending is defined and a random selection of beginning and middle plays is allowed. However, when playing against an opponent with any experience, the computer will not win very often (if at all), since the opening plays virtually control the game.

## CHECKERS, CHESS, AND OTHER TOPICS

For more complicated problems, a combination of tree searching and local optimization can be used. The search is limited to as many branches as are compatible with the capacity of the computer and the time available. The possible actions are evaluated on the basis of as many tests as the programmer desires or his ingenuity suggests. Sometimes called the *search-scan* method, this technique is believed to have been first used by Newell, Shaw, and Simon in a theorem-proving program.[10] A scheme of this type has been used by A. L. Samuel to program a computer to play checkers.[16] In addition, by evaluating successive games using different optimization criteria, it is possible to make the program adaptive and thus develop a capability which is very close to human intelligence.

Chess is also a game which has appealed to the developers of heuristic techniques.[3,11,18] Here, even searching the game tree a few levels becomes an impossible task (it has been estimated that there are some $10^{120}$ possible branches), and it is necessary to restrict the search to those moves which appear plausible or for which the opponent has only a limited number of replies.

Yet another variation of the game tree has been applied to programs for proving geometrical theorems.[6,7] Starting with the result as the apex of the tree, the program forms branches on the basis of rules and other theorems until it forms the branches which correspond to the initial assumptions of the theorem to be proved. This is essentially a process of induction. As with chess, care must be taken to limit the procedure to plausible deductions, otherwise we may search the whole space of propositions before arriving at the desired positions.

The problem of forming a connective between specified sets of data chosen from any general area, i.e., theory formation, is also under investigation;[1,2] an adaptive search program for playing *battleships* in a $10 \times 10$ matrix on the basis of computer calculated probabilities of the ships occupying certain positions has been reported;[15] a program called SAINT which solves freshman calculus has been devised;[19] and heuristic programming has also been applied to business problems.[20]

Programs for playing games, proving theorems, and the like are the elementary blocks on which one day we may build a technique for solving some of the larger problems of society. Developments to date have been concerned with well-defined situations in which the status at any time can be given in binary terms, and the overall objective is obvious and relatively easily defined. The next step must be to expand the principles uncovered and to develop a generalized approach to problem solving.

## GENERAL PROBLEM SOLVER

A start in this direction has been made in a program known as General Problem Solver (GPS).[12,13] In this approach data is divided into two types: specific information, which sets the situation, describes the task, and provides collateral data; and the general processes which may be used for problem solving. The former is unique to the problem at hand, or may be related to the problem class, while the latter are general operation which can be used to solve any problem.

As an example, the detection of forgeries, whether of bank notes, checks, or paintings, involves the same intellectual operation of comparing the suspect document with the original (general process); however, the detailed knowledge of bank notes, signatures, and painting techniques is quite different (specific information). An expert in one speciality may not be an expert in the others. However, because of the commonality of data concerned with inks, pigments, basic materials, etc., and the use of similar intellectual processes, the man whose major job is the detection of counterfeit money will be much more helpful in detecting a forged painting than a tyro.

The storage of specific information requires an extremely large memory, with the consequent problems of organization and access. In GPS, access to this data is provided by *discrimination trees* which perform two processes; *discrimination,* i.e., classifying the input information on the basis of its content and characteristics, so as to identify similar data stored in the computer; and *familiarization,* i.e., detection of patterns in the input information and testing the current task for similarity with previous tasks, so as to provide correlating or historical data.

The general processes which are common to all of the tasks attempted by GPS are *planning, problem solving organization,* and *means-end analysis.*

*Planning* involves the development of a skeleton solution taking only the major features of the problem into account. The complete solution is then obtained by adding detail, piece by piece. As an example of this technique, suppose it is necessary to optimize the performance of a particular system which depends on several parameters, two of which are much more important than the rest. As a first approximation, the system can be optimized on the basis of the important parameters. The other conditions can then be incorporated in the trial solution by iterating around significant points until a reasonable approximation to an optimum solution is obtained.

*Problem solving organization* is concerned with the detailed steps in the solution. In checkers or chess this portion of GPS would be concerned with searching the game tree, scanning and evaluating the data, determining the parameters which should be measured in order to assess the effectiveness of proposed moves, and controlling the degree of lookahead so as to optimize the confidence in the solution and the solution time.

*Means-end analysis* is concerned with the gross differences between any given situation and a reference or desired situation. By selecting sets of operators which are related to these differences, this portion of GPS, seeks to change the one situation into the other. Thus, to return to an example used in Chapter 1, GPS might attempt to prove the equivalence of the differential and integral forms of Maxwell's equations by detecting the difference in the mathematical operators and using the relation

$$\iint \frac{d}{dt} = \int \qquad (5.2)$$

and such other conversions as must be provided in the initial statement of the problem.

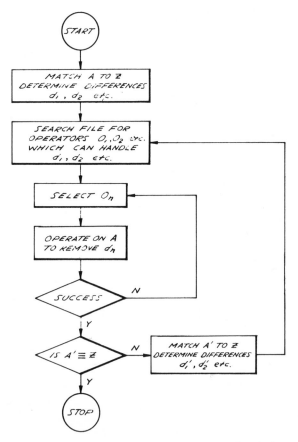

Figure 5–8. Routine to illustrate GPS means-end analysis

The principle of this technique is shown in Fig. 5–8. The initial expression is represented as $A$, and the required expression is designated $Z$. The expressions are compared to determine the differences $d_1$, $d_2$, ... etc.; and operators $O_1$, $O_2$, ... etc., which are related to these differences, are selected from the file containing functions appropriate to the problem. One of these operators is then used to transform $A$ into $A'$. If $A' \equiv Z$, the routine is completed. If $A' \not\equiv Z$, then another operator is used in an attempt to reduce the remaining differences. If any of the operators fails to remove part of the difference, they are discarded. In this manner, provided we have a sufficient set of operators, $A$ is eventually reduced to $Z$. By suitable record keeping within the computer, orders of priority can be established for application of the operators so that the program eventually becomes proficient in performing the transformation.

Not all of the processing functions contained in GPS are necessarily used in the solution of a particular problem. In fact, it is more than likely that the solution will concentrate in one area or the other. With such a general purpose capability, however, it is possible to use GPS to start to solve large-scale engineering, business, or economic problems.

## DISCUSSION

It has been said elsewhere in this book that a learning system is really an extension of the designer's intelligence and that the best that we can expect is that it behave in the manner of a well-trained, but not very bright, analyst. This is particularly true of the programs just discussed, for their very structure depends on the program writer, his knowledge of problem solving techniques, and the capability of the computer. No machine can be expected to generate instructions which cannot fit the framework supplied by the programmer, nor can it invent new circuit connections or improve the hardware available.

A compiler provides the capability of a well-trained programmer or coder because all possible connectives between the input language and the machine code have been included. The preparation of these programs requires a high degree of competence on the part of the analyst.

Heuristic programs represent the same general class of capability although the fictitious, *well-trained, not very bright,* analyst is a little brighter than his compiler counterpart, for he is able to evaluate the present position and to select a course on the basis of the logical rules supplied by the human director. The virtue of these programs is that they are relatively omniscient and are able to do a much more thorough job of searching and evaluating than is normally done by a human.

The uses to which a computer can be put are limited by the communication difficulties between man and machine. While FORTRAN and other languages are a great step forward, they still require that the programmer specify the major steps to the problem solution. What is needed to improve computer utility still further is an even stronger language which will accept general statements such as "Solve $y = ax^2 + b$ for $x_0(c)x_n$." Perhaps a combination of the compiler art and heuristic programming can achieve this.

If we had a large enough computer (and sufficient patience), we could theoretically store all of the data which forms our experience, and provide program loops which would describe all of the algorithms we have developed for meeting common situations. With proper organization, the result would be a simulation of the passive intellect (see Chapter 1). However, as with the hardware models described earlier, implementation of this scheme is impossible. The size of the storage would be beyond all practical consideration; and, even if a tree structure were used, the probability of being able to recall specific data on demand, in a reasonable time, would appear to be very small. Further, the chance of being able to state all of the algorithms in analytical terms is remote. A basic assumption to our whole plan is that man is a completely logical being whose actions can be reduced to a mathematical description; it would be very surprising if this were true.

## REFERENCES

1. S. Amarel, "An Approach to Automatic Theory Formation," *Principles of Self-Organization,* H. von Foerster and G. W. Zopf, eds., Pergamon Press, New York, 1962, pp. 443–483.
2. ———, "On the Automatic Formation of a Computer Program Which Represents a Theory," *Self-Organizing Systems—1962,* M. C. Yovitts, G. T. Jacobi, and G. D. Goldstein, eds., Spartan Books, Washington, D.C., 1962, pp. 107–175.
3. A. Bernstein, "A Chess Playing Program for the IBM 704," *Proceedings, Western Joint Computer Conference (AFIPS), 1958,* pp. 157–159.
4. B. G. Farley and W. A. Clark, "Simulation of Self-Organizing Systems by Digital Computer," *IRE Transactions on Information Theory,* vol. IT-4, 1954, pp. 76–84.
5. E. A. Feigenbaum and J. Feldman, eds., *Computers and Thought,* McGraw-Hill, New York, 1964.
6. H. L. Gelernter, "Realization of a Geometry-Proving Machine," *Proceedings, International Conference on Information Processing,* UNESCO, 1959, pp. 273–282. Reprinted in Feigenbaum and Feldman, *op. cit.,* pp. 134–152.

7. _____, J. R. Hansen, and D. W. Loveland, "Empirical Explorations of the Geometry-Theorem Proving Machine," *Proceedings, Western Joint Computer Conference (AFIPS),* 1960, pp. 143–147. Reprinted in Feigenbaum and Feldman, *op. cit.,* pp. 153–163.

8. M. H. Halstead, *Machine Independent Computer Programming,* Spartan Books, Washington, D.C., 1962.

9. O. Morganstern and J. von Neumann, *The Theory of Games and Economic Behavior,* Princeton University Press, Princeton, N.J., 1953.

10. A. Newell and H. A. Simon, "Empirical Explorations with the Logic Theory Machine: A Case Study in Heuristics," *Proceedings, Western Joint Computer Conference (AFIPS),* 1957, pp. 218–239. Reprinted in Feigenbaum and Feldman, *op. cit.,* pp. 109–133.

11. _____, J. C. Shaw, and H. A. Simon, "Chess Playing Programs and the Problem of Complexity," *IBM Journal of Research and Development,* vol. 2, 1958, pp. 320–335. Reprinted in Feigenbaum and Feldman, *op. cit.,* pp. 39–70.

12. _____, _____, and _____, "Elements of a Theory of Human Problem Solving," *Psychological Review,* vol. 65, 1958, pp. 151–166.

13. _____ and H. A. Simon, "GPS: A Program that Simulates Human Thought," *Lernende Automaten,* R. Oldenbourg, Munich, 1961. Reprinted in Fiegenbaum and Feldman, *op. cit.,* pp. 279–293.

14. W. Orchard-Hays, "The Evolution of Programming Systems," *Proceedings, IRE,* vol. 49, 1961, pp. 283–295.

15. S. R. Petrick, T. V. Griffith, and H. M. Willett, "An Adaptive Search Program for the Game of Battleships," *Artificial Intelligence,* IEEE Publication S-142, 1963, pp. 146–156.

16. A. L. Samuel, "Some Studies in Machine Learning Using the Game of Checkers," *IBM Journal of Research and Development,* vol. 3, 1959, pp. 211–229. Reprinted in Feigenbaum and Feldman, *op. cit.,* pp. 71–105.

17. H. A. Simon and A. Newell, "Information Processing in Computer and Man," *American Scientist,* vol. 52, 1964, pp. 281–300.

18. _____ and P. A. Simon, "Trial and Error Search in Solving Difficult Problems: Evidence from the Game of Chess," *Behavioral Science,* vol. 7, 1962, pp. 425–429.

19. J. Slagle, "A Heuristic Program that Solves Symbolic Integration Problems in Freshman Calculus," *Computers and Thought,* E. A. Feigenbaum and J. Feldman, eds., McGraw-Hill, New York, 1964, pp. 191–203.

20. F. M. Tonge, "Summary of a Heuristic Line Balancing Procedure," *Management Science,* vol. 7, 1960, pp. 21–42. Reprinted in Feigenbaum and Feldman, *op. cit.,* pp. 168–190.

Chapter 6

# RELIABLE NETWORKS

One of the outstanding features of the human brain is its reliability. After a period of growth and training, it normally operates continuously for some 40–60 years, fulfilling bodily needs, controlling necessary functions, and supporting all of the intellectual processes required for a full adult life. Such performance is achieved despite the continual destruction of cells by minor hemorrhages and aging processes. In fact, even certain surgical procedures and the removal of sections of the gray matter may have no discernible effect.

The ability to operate in the presence of these imperfections can only be explained on the basis of redundant cells and the multitude of random interconnections known to exist. For, if each and every cell were charged with a unique function, the destruction of even one cell should, in principle, be detectable; certainly the destruction of large numbers of cells would be noticed. Similarly, if the interconnections were well-ordered, a local catastrophe could be expected to destroy a large number of connections of the same kind, with consequent impairment of function.

As it is, each neuron is randomly connected to an average of perhaps 100 other neurons, some of which may be close by and others many neuron layers away. Thus, the destruction of even a large number of connections in a particular area will affect only a small fraction of the connections in any subnetwork.

It is possible that the slow loss of neurons is compensated by an unconscious retraining process, in which the memory trace is reestablished in other neurons so as to permit continuation of a particular skill. Somewhat analogous behavior has been shown to be possible in an artificial learning network.[1] Specifically, if the statistical elements of a binary logical element fail in random fashion; and, after each failuure, the network is allowed to reorganize, in an optimum manner, the percentage of all possible functions which can still be formed is much greater than the percentage of the network remaining (for small values of percentage failure). Some theoretical results are shown in Fig. 6–1.

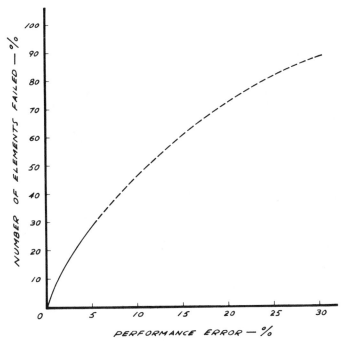

Figure 6–1.  Retention of performance of learning network provided optimum reorganization can be effected after each failure

## VON NEUMANN'S BUNDLES

The number of fibers in a neural network may be two orders of magnitude greater than the number of neurons, i.e., a human brain probably contains some $10^{12}$ fibers.  While there is no direct evidence that this multiplicity of connecting pathways contributes to the unique reliability of the assemblage, von Neumann has demonstrated that such can be the case for artificial networks.[5]

Suppose that the signal connections in a neural network are replaced by bundles of $n$ lines, so that, if some fraction of these lines greater than $(1 - a)$ is excited (where a $< \frac{1}{2}$), the signal is designated as 1, and if some fraction less than $a$ is excited, the signal is designated as 0.  Such bundles can be randomly interconnected by majority organs to provide a device which will have a reliability greater than that of the individual signal channels.  Random interconnection is necessary so as to ensure a high probability of the excitation of at least $(1 - a)n$ of the lines in a majority of the input bundles, resulting in the excitation of a majority of the connections to each majority element, and in the excitation of a high proportion of the output lines.

For practical majority elements, a certain probability of malfunction must be anticipated. If this is less than the improvement effected by the bundling technique, then additional majority elements can be expected to improve the performance of the network so that the overall reliability is greater than the reliability of an individual element. A possible construction is shown in Fig. 6–2. This principle is not restricted to majority elements, but may be used with formal neurons and other devices.[4] It should be pointed out, however, that the additional majority elements have as many inputs as there are lines in the input bundles. Since maintenance of a stable threshold level becomes more difficult as the number of inputs increases, the probability of error in the majority elements becomes greater as the number of lines in each bundle increases. Thus we have two opposing effects which set an upper limit to the size of the bundles in this construction.

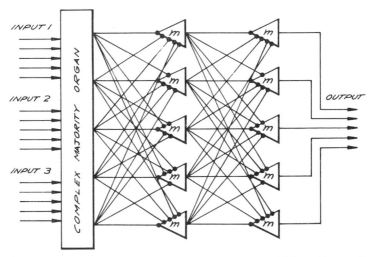

Figure 6–2. Method of improving network reliability by addition of layers of Majority elements

## SELF-REPAIR

Conventional electronic equipment and all other man-made devices are capable of performing their design function for a limited time—until one or more components fail. By suitable preventive maintenance and rapid substitution of new parts, should a catastrophic failure occur, the basic equipment can be kept operating indefinitely. Eventually, none of the original parts will remain in the equipment. If this type of operation can be simulated by a system, then we have a mechanism for self-repair.

Needless to say, such a mechanism has not been implemented in any general fashion and is very much in the theoretical stage. Two models have been postulated for self-repairing systems.[2,3] One, called a *tesselation* model, comprises a spatial array of contiguous cells which contain logic elements or other circuitry. Initially, a certain number of cells are activated in such a manner that they form a system which can perform some useful function. Other cells, distributed throughout the matrix, are inactive, although they can be activated by appropriate signals from their neighbors. As cells fail, these signals are generated, and the system continues to operate with a newly activated cell in place of the one which failed. Obviously, the resources of any practical cell array are finite so that a time must come when the system has used up all of its resources and fails for good.

An elementary form of this technique is employed in certain computers and control systems intended for spaceborne or other high-performance missions. Here, the critical components are implemented in parallel so that, as soon as the primary component fails, or shows signs of poor performance, a second component is connected and takes over the function.

The other self-repairing technique, called a *kinematic* model, comprises a system which performs a useful function and which, in addition, can control suitable mechanisms which can select and connect together new components so as to reproduce its own system organization. Once a second system is built, it can assume the responsibilities of the first system, and proceed to build a third system, and so on. Obviously, assuming such a capability can be developed in the first system, and an unlimited supply of new components is available, this mechanism is self-perpetuating. The problem, of course, is to build the first system, and then to ensure that newly made components are available as required. If a limited stockpile is postulated to exist when the first system is built, the mechanism can function only until the stockpile is exhausted or the remaining components in the stockpile have exceeded their shelf life.

Such self-repair mechanisms may eventually achieve practical status. Certainly the tesselation model appears feasible, and under certain (not too complex) circumstances, we may be able to implement the kinematic approach. Both undoubtedly will be finite in application, and there will have to be urgent reasons for their use to outweigh the economic disadvantages of such schemes.

## DISCUSSION

Reliability is an important consideration in any engineering program. In fact, the ability to design and construct equipment which will operate with predictable performance for a stated length of time is a distinguishing feature of the good engineer. Another feature is a healthy regard for the cost of the final equipment. It is almost axiomatic that the more reliable an equipment must be, the more expensive it is, and it is doubtful that the expense of building a system which can perform useful work and also reproduce itself will ever be justifiable, since man is conveniently available. Similarly, proliferation of signal leads and majority elements may well be an unwarranted complication, although the basic principles involved can very well be prudently employed at key points in any equipment.

## REFERENCES

1. E. B. Carne, E. M. Connelly, P. H. Halpern, and B. A. Logan, "A Self-Organizing Binary Logical Network," *Biological Prototypes and Synthetic Systems*, E. E. Bernard and M. R. Kare, eds., Plenum Press, New York, 1962, vol. 1, pp. 311–330.
2. L. Lofgren, "Self-Repair as the Limit for Automatic Error Correction," *Principles of Self-Organization*, H. von Foerster and G. W. Zopf, eds., Pergamon Press, New York, 1962, pp. 181–228.
3. ———, "Kinematic and Tesselation Models of Self-Repair," *Biological Prototypes and Synthetic Systems*, E. E. Bernard and M. R. Kare, eds., Plenum Press, New York, 1962, vol. 1, pp. 342–369.
4. L. A. M. Verbeek, "On Error Minimizing Neural Nets," *Principles of Self-Organization*, H. von Foerster and G. W. Zopf, eds., Pergamon Press, New York, 1962, pp. 121–133.
5. J. von Neumann, "Probabilistic Logics and the Synthesis of Reliable Organisms from Unreliable Components," *Automata Studies*, C. E. Shannon and J. McCarthy, eds., Princeton University Press, Princeton, N.J., 1956, pp. 43–98.
6. ———, "The General and Logical Theory of Automata," *Cerebral Mechanisms in Behavior*, John Wiley, New York, 1957.

## IN CONCLUSION

> ... but Patience, to prevent
> That murmur, soon replies, God doth not need
> Either man's work, or his own gifts ...

—MILTON

It is now up to the patient reader to apply the principles described in this book to his specific problems. Only in this way will we be able to forge a new approach to the design of electronic systems. One thing is clear. Any attempt to reproduce a human brain by extant technology is doomed to failure because of our inability to reproduce the intricate complexities and to simulate the detailed mechanisms of any but the simplest neurons. It is quite unlikely that our knowledge encompasses all of the subtleties of interconnection required, and our models are certainly not much more than first attempts at producing neuromimes. Even if suitable techniques *were* available, all we would achieve by a slavish modeling of the brain would be an extremely complicated logical device. Without the secret of *life*, we cannot hope to construct an automaton which would mimic the wisdom of Plato, the inquisitiveness of Newton, the inspiration of John Kennedy, or the leadership of Winston Churchill.

What we can hope to do, however, is to devise electronic systems which can operate in restricted areas performing those tasks which are currently delegated to humans, not because they require the intrinsic faculties possessed by a man, but because, heretofore, their performance has been beyond the capability of conventional electronic systems. It is to be hoped that the application of these techniques will provide the keys to develop new approaches to the technology which will be required to support the continuing scientific revolution of the twentieth century.

It is all too apparent that any major advance in the development of artificial intelligence per se depends on the state of our knowledge of biological phenomena. A breakthrough in this field could provide the design principles for a significant improvement in learning systems. We should not be too proud to admit this dependence, for biological systems are the only tools which are able to perform the functions we seek to imitate. To start on an independent approach, because the problems of experimental biology seem too great, would be to abandon the only guide we have. To ignore a design which has functioned for centuries, and which was undoubtedly derived from an intelligence greater than ours, would be foolhardy.

Perhaps, as electronic neuromimes become more representative of their physical counterparts, advances in electronics will be of help to the biologist in unraveling the mysteries of the nervous system. We must surely hope so. As for psychology, the further development of computer programs and of machine independent languages, may help to formalize the concepts of learning theory and of other mental processes. However, there is much to be done by the computer analyst in this direction, and probably much more to be done by the psychologist, before a useful exchange of ideas can be consummated.

The most serious limitation to our work, and perhaps that which prevents us from attaining better performance, may reside in the choice of the analytical and experimental techniques used to simulate the nervous system. These are, after all, the ones with which we are most familiar and which represent the state of electronics today. For instance, there does not really seem to be any good reason why the nervous system should operate on the basis of the laws of Boolean algebra, or should only contain two-state devices. Such is the implication of some of our models. Nor is there any reason why a system based only on threshold logic or statistical decisions should be any closer to the real world.

These techniques are products of minds trained in mathematics and scientific method, and in bending the real world to fit their constructs, we may be limiting the ultimate product. They are convenient for describing one facet, or another, of the observed behavior, and they are applied according to the interest, or early training, of the investigator. Just as light can be characterized as corpuscular or wavelike, and certain phenomena can be explained by one representation and not the other, it may be that all we can do within the framework of current scientific method is construct limited models for particular situations. If this is true, we may be forever prevented from achieving an adequate description of the nature of intelligence. The precedents of atomic physics and astronomy, to name but two areas in which there appear to be well-defined limits to our ultimate knowledge, may well support this opinion.

There is no question but that we have a long way to go before such limitations become apparent. To return to more immediate possibilities, it can be confidently predicted that continued work in this field will yield useful and probably unexpected results, which will greatly affect the design philosophy and implementation of future electronic systems.

# INDEX

148